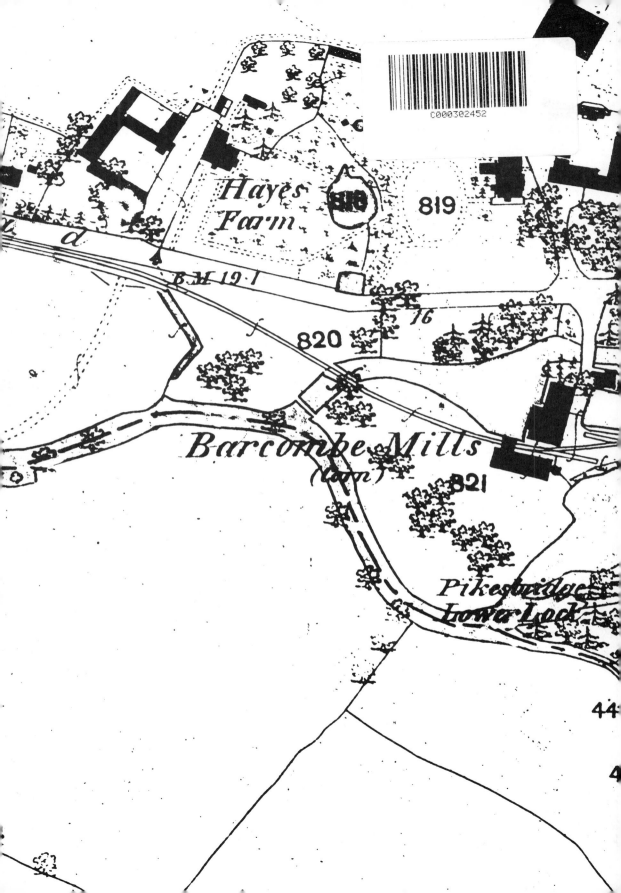

Hayes
Farm

d

819

BM 19·1

16

820

Barcombe Mills
(corn)

821

Pikesbridge
Lower Lock

44

4

WATERMILLS of SUSSEX

(VOLUME I — EAST SUSSEX)

FRONT COVER: Isfield Mill in 1910.
(BH)

Tickerage Mill in 1904. (BT)

WATERMILLS
of SUSSEX

(VOLUME I — EAST SUSSEX)

BY

DEREK STIDDER & COLIN SMITH

BARON
MCMXCVII

PUBLISHED BY BARON BIRCH FOR
QUOTES LIMITED
AND PRODUCED BY KEY COMPOSITION,
SOUTH MIDLANDS LITHOPLATES,
CHENEY & SONS, HILLMAN PRINTERS (FROME) LIMITED
AND WBC BOOK MANUFACTURERS

ISBN 0 86023 569 6

CONTENTS

ACKNOWLEDGEMENTS

We are indebted to the many organisations, mill owners and individuals who have patiently supplied us with information, both from public and private sources. In particular, we must thank Frank Gregory for drawing on his immense knowledge of Sussex mills; Mr R. Hawksley for his constructive criticism and for providing additional research material and to David Tomlinson for providing maps and diagrams.

The staff and members of the following organisations have assisted us with our research: Wealden Postcard Club; Sussex Industrial Archaeological Society; the Wind and Watermill Section of the SPAB; East Sussex Record Office; Brighton Reference Library; British Engineerium; Science Museum Library, for permission to consult the Simmons papers for Sussex and the Dennis Sanders Collection and, finally, the Uckfield and District Preservation Society. A word must also go to F. W. Mays & Co Ltd of Dorking, who unwittingly provided transport to all the sites mentioned in this book.

Photographs are an important part of this book and we are grateful, in particular, to Alan Stoyel, Frank Gregory, Roger Packham, Mrs Vivian Ewing and the SPAB for permission to reproduce photographs from their collections.

Also, specific thanks are given to the mill owners who have, without exception, allowed us to roam freely around their property to record and photograph as required.

Key to Caption Credits

AS	Alan Stoyel	LF	Lydia Foster
AT	Ann Turner	RP	Roger Packham
BH	Brian Hart	TD	Thomas Dadswell
BRL	Brighton Reference Libary	SPAB	Society for the Protection of Ancient Buildings
BT	Bertha Terry		
CW	Charles Warren	VE	Vivian Ewing
FG	Frank Gregory		

All other photographs are from the authors' collection

FOREWORD *by Frank Gregory*

Here is a book about the unknown, for while a windmill waves its sails on the top of the hill, the watermill is far more elusive, tucked away in a deep wooded valley, and it is to this that the present authors have turned their attention.

Derek Stidder has already studied the watermills of Surrey in an earlier book and now attention has been given to East Sussex. Despite the number of windmills, there are far more watermills and these have been recorded, together with the families who ran and maintained them.

Although no watermill in East Sussex is at present in full commercial use, several have been restored to grinding order as part of a heritage presentation.

DEDICATION

To Moira and Jane for their support and tolerance.

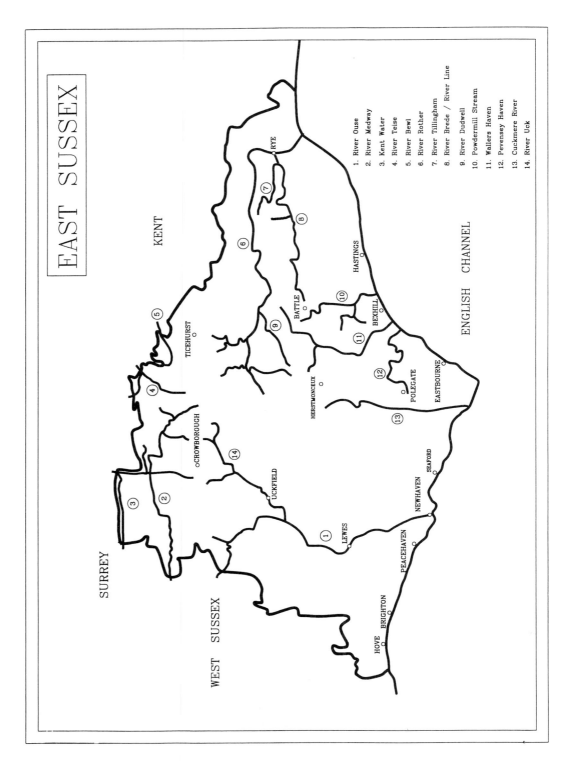

EAST SUSSEX

SURREY

KENT

WEST SUSSEX

ENGLISH CHANNEL

1. River Ouse
2. River Medway
3. Kent Water
4. River Teise
5. River Bewl
6. River Rother
7. River Tillingham
8. River Brede / River Line
9. River Dudwell
10. Powdermill Stream
11. Wallers Haven
12. Pevensey Haven
13. Cuckmere River
14. River Uck

RYE

TICEHURST

CROWBOROUGH

UCKFIELD

HERSTMONCEUX

POLEGATE

EASTBOURNE

BATTLE

HASTINGS

BEXHILL

SEAFORD

NEWHAVEN

PEACEHAVEN

LEWES

HOVE

BRIGHTON

INTRODUCTION

Sussex has been divided into two separate administrative counties for centuries with the county towns of Lewes and Chichester respectively, although Sussex retained a single Lord Lieutenant, High Sheriff and Assizes. The Quarter Sessions, which governed the counties, had divided Sussex into two, while later the Local Government Act of 1972 moved the county boundary eastwards and important towns such as Haywards Heath, East Grinstead, Burgess Hill and the surrounding villages became part of West Sussex.

The coastline of East Sussex stretches from Broomhill, near Rye, in the east, through to Portslade-by-Sea. Further inland its northern boundary is with Surrey and Kent, enclosing the high ridges of the Ashdown Forest, although there is now little forest left. The South Downs feature prominently in the county, with Ditchling Beacon at 813ft the highest point in East Sussex, and are only broken by the river valleys of the Ouse and the Cuckmere. The countryside of the county is varied with its open tracts of reclaimed land and deep wooded valleys, the later lending themselves to deep and easily formed expansive millponds.

The geology of East Sussex is dominated by the chalk of the South Downs, under which are narrow layers of upper and lower greensand. It was the Weald clay, further inland, which caused severe transport problems in the winter, prompting the millers to use river transport wherever possible. The Ouse Navigation was particularly popular until the advent of the railways. The iron industry certainly left its mark on the vegetation and countryside of East Sussex but now leisure pursuits and agriculture form the principal 'industries' of the county.

As this volume concentrates on the history of the watermill in East Sussex in particular, general watermill history and details of machinery operation have been kept to a minimum. The principal watermill industry of East Sussex was flour milling but the gunpowder industry and, to a lesser degree, papermaking feature prominently at the sites concerned. We have managed to locate and visit the 90 water powered sites in the county but of these, 58 are no more than sites with few remains, or a subtle change in vegetation, to indicate the position of a once important site. Of the remaining sites only Bartley Mill at Frant continues producing flour on a commercial basis using traditional methods, while the two other working mills at Michelham Priory and at Park Mill, Burwash produce flour on a casual basis mainly to sell to visitors. Nevertheless, there are sufficient remains at most of the extant former mill buildings to understand the method of operation and appreciate the importance of what is now a long forgotten industry.

There are several books detailing the history of the windmills in Sussex, but nothing similar exists concerning the watermills of the county. As there are at least 230 watermill sites, it has been decided to separate the research into two volumes, ie: East Sussex and West Sussex. This book relates to the watermills of East Sussex and chronicles their history and development over the centuries.

9

Bishopstone Tide Mills and the village in 1853. (BRL)

THE WATERMILL IN EAST SUSSEX

The majority of watermills in the county are small and mainly contained 3-pairs of stones. There were, though, notable exceptions to this — bearing in mind the size and magnitude of Robertsbridge Mill and the much lamented Bishopstone Tide Mills. All the mills that stood in the county were constructed in local materials, and mostly were timber-framed with brick to the first floor (Michelham Priory Mill is an excellent example). As there were numerous small brickworks throughout Sussex, many mills constructed in the early 18th century took advantage of this accordingly. The one disadvantage of using brick was the brick and tile tax introduced in September 1784. Like any tax it was very unpopular. It was introduced at the conclusion of the expensive War of American Independence to provide much-needed funds and was further increased in 1794 and 1805. In 1850 the brick tax was abolished, but by then few watermills were being built and it was because of this tax that the timber-framed mill was used throughout South-East England.

The Weald of Sussex was once under oak forest but, following the emergence of the iron industry, the demand for charcoal cleared great swathes through the Sussex countryside. Oak also became the principal wood used in the construction of the country mill, while elm was predominantly used for the waterwheels and paddles. It was with the introduction of the roller mill that the structural capability of the mill had to be increased, and brick-built mills became more common (a good surviving example is Uckfield Mill). Sadly, disused mills were often demolished soon after closure or else were converted for residential use, as was Shortbridge Mill near Uckfield.

THE RIVERS

The availability of water power throughout most of the county led to a number of tributaries being used to drive the 90 known mill sites. It should be borne in mind, however, that many of these rivers were far bigger than they are today.

East Sussex has three main principal rivers — the Ouse, Cuckmere and Rother. The Ouse and the Rother and their tributaries were navigable and the Ouse became a navigation of 25 locks. Other important rivers such as the Medway are shared with Kent, but nevertheless 11 watermills were sited within the county, with Crowborough New Mill one of the most intriguing sites in Sussex.

The transport of materials and goods through the Weald was difficult. In the winter the gault clay became an impassable muddy morass, while in the summer the ruts from the previous months caused equal difficulties. The much-heralded Turnpike Trusts did little to improve the condition of the trackways throughout the county, but the advantage of transporting goods by water has been recognised from Roman times and many of the larger rivers were regularly used by small boats based at Lewes, Newhaven and Rye.

OUSE NAVIGATION

The River Ouse was the most important river in East Sussex. Rising on the outskirts of St Leonards Forest, near Horsham, it flows over 40 miles to its estuary at Newhaven.

In the 18th century the Ouse below Lewes was a tidal navigation, while above Lewes small boats could reach as far as Maresfield Forge. In 1788 William Jessop was commissioned to investigate the possibility of making the Ouse above Lewes navigable for some distance. He also suggested a possible navigation past Barcombe Mill, extending to a point just beyond the Cuckfield-Balcombe road, almost to its source. It was not until 1812 that the Navigation was completed, with a length of 22½ miles and 25 locks. Also in this year a short branch was built to Shortbridge to serve the Uckfield area. Understandably, the 15 established mills near to the Navigation in East Sussex saw the opportunity to increase their trading limits and most of them profited accordingly.

The Ouse Navigation was mainly an agricultural waterway with its upstream traffic of chalk, coal and stone and its return traffic of agricultural produce. It maintained a small but regular trade until the London and Brighton Railway was built. Ironically, the Navigation was used to transport the building materials for the large railway viaduct at Balcombe, completed in 1841. The demise of the Navigation was further hastened when a railway branch line was opened between Uckfield and Lewes in 1858.

In 1851 the upper part of the Navigation above Lindfield became disused, with the remainder above Lewes suffering the same fate later. The present River Ouse is now a fraction of its former size and the disused and overgrown locks stand as a mute reminder of its former days.

RIVER ROTHER AND RIVER BREDE

The eastern River Rother rises near Rotherfield and at one time the river ran to New Romney, but the great storm of 1287 totally changed its course. The river was used in early times and became navigable without the need for locks. The Rother was navigable to Bodiam, Udiam and beyond, with the building stone for the famous castle being transported to the site by water in the late 14th century. Later on, iron ore and iron from the local furnaces were the principal cargoes, with collection and distribution from Udiam. The carriage of corn, flour, timber and other provisions became the main income — especially as there were 11 watermills situated along its length. The nearby River Brede was also used for the carriage of iron ore for use in the local furnace. From 1747 until 1766, for example, barges came up the river from Rye harbour loaded with iron ore and groceries for local shopkeepers and returned with guns and shot. In 1770 the Brede gunpowder mills replaced the iron furnace site, and subsequently gunpowder was carried to Rye — a development that must have been viewed with trepidation by local residents along the route.

The decline of both navigations began in 1933 when the needs of land drainage were given priority over the maintenance of a navigable depth.

RIVER CUCKMERE

The River Cuckmere rises near Heathfield and enters the English Channel at Cuckmere Haven.

Towards the end of the 18th century there was a proposal to build a canal from the River Ouse, below Lewes, to Hellingly and Horsebridge, but it appears that this proposal received little support. However, this did not restrict the development of some of the 10 watermills recorded, of which Horsebridge Mill was one of the biggest with its extant large diameter waterwheel.

RIVER UCK

This was a prolific watermill river with 10 mills once working over a relatively short length. Water levels were especially good and large mills, such as those at Isfield, Uckfield and Hempstead, continued working well into the present century.

There were other notable rivers and streams that were heavily used. The Powdermill Stream (formerly the River Asten) provided the capacity over centuries to power the gunpowder mills at Battle, Peppering Eye and Crowhurst.

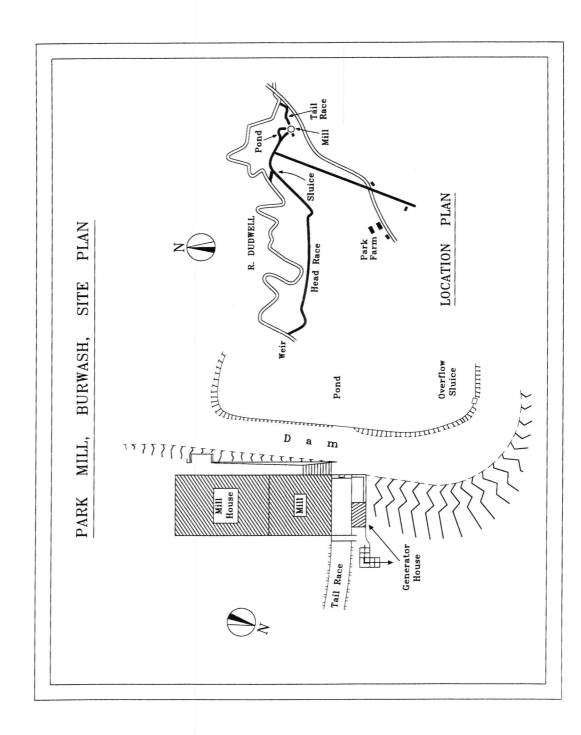

PARK MILL, BURWASH, SITE PLAN

LOCATION PLAN

N

R. DUDWELL

Weir

Head Race

Sluice

Pond

Mill Race

Tail Race

Park Farm

Pond

Dam

Overflow Sluice

N

Mill House

Mill

Tail Race

Generator House

14

THE MILLER'S CRAFT

The waterwheel was the sole power source in any watermill and every piece of machinery was driven directly or indirectly from it.

Since early times, civilisations have been attempting to develop and gain increased efficiency in an effort to harness water power. It is accepted that the Romans first introduced the geared waterwheel into Britain to provide flour for the conquering troops. The early waterwheels were probably of the undershot variety, driving basic machinery on a method that was unchanged for centuries. It was with the introduction of the geared watermill, using a vertical waterwheel, that the craft of the miller became more efficient and sophisticated. Apart from those mills near the Kent border, the majority of the waterwheels in East Sussex were externally mounted and overshot.

The various types of waterwheel found in East Sussex are classified according to the point of entry of the water onto the wheel — in other words, undershot, breastshot (including high and low), overshot and pitchback.

Undershot The undershot waterwheel was most appropriate in low lying areas where there was an all-year-round supply of water. The wheels are operated by water passing below or under the wheels. Typically, the wheel is adjusted to be just submerged and as the water flows downstream it strikes the paddles and turns the wheel, using kinetic energy. Apart from the Pevensey Levels, there are few such low-lying areas in the rest of the county. The only known site where such wheels were used was at the Bishopstone Tidemill, where three (15ft diameter) wheels drove 16-pairs of stones and large millponds were constructed to hold the incoming tide.

Overshot This type of wheel is driven by water passing just over the top of the wheel to fill the buckets. The weight of the water then unbalances the wheel and sets it in motion using potential energy. Once the wheel is turning only a small amount of water is required to keep it in motion and it was usual to construct a millpond to gain the necessary height and water capacity required. The overshot waterwheel was commonly found in East Sussex and one of the best examples is at Plumpton Mill, where the 12ft diameter iron overshot wheel, manufactured in 1889 in Lewes, is a superb working example of its type.

Breastshot In a breastshot wheel the water falls onto the blades or buckets so that the weight of water turns the wheels. The term 'breastshot' refers to a wheel where the water strikes the wheel at axle level, and the variation 'high or low' refers to the water coming in just above or below the level of the axle. A breastshot wheel was normally used where a substantial water supply could be ponded and controlled, but in East Sussex this was not always the case. The extant waterwheels at Horsebridge Mill (17ft by 8ft) and Hempstead Mill (16ft) are both low breastshot wheels, being powered directly from a river rather than a pond.

Pitchback This type of waterwheel works in a similar way to a high breastshot wheel in that the water is fed to a position just below the top of the wheel. In most cases this type of wheel would rotate in the direction of the tail race, thus avoiding backwatering. At Shortbridge Mill the wheel is fed from downstream by using an unusual pentrough arrangement, converting it from the more common overshot waterwheel.

TURBINES

In principle, turbines are based on the horizontal or 'Greek Mill', except that the wheel is enclosed, with carefully shaped blades. The turbine became commercially viable during the 19th century and such systems replaced the waterwheel at many mills throughout the country. The installation of a turbine required alteration to the millrace and to the means of transmitting power to the machinery, since most types operated below water level. One of the few examples of such a system can be found at Isfield Mill where a turbine, manufactured by Joseph J. Armfield, was installed in 1905. The handwheel and indicator control panel were last seen standing proudly among bags of dog biscuits.

LAYOUT OF WATERCOURSES AND MILLPONDS

Selecting a site for a watermill was crucial and depended on the surrounding landscape. This was particularly so in East Sussex, where extensive hills and valleys exist across most of the county. It is only at the Pevensey Levels that flat and marshy land abounds, but this area was of no use to the watermiller.

Of the 90 known mill sites, 65 were driven by ponded water with the overshot waterwheel predominantly used to gain the maximum mechanical efficiency. As the flow of water from the rivers of East Sussex was not sufficient to drive a mill, it was the normal practice to construct a millpond. A causeway or embankment was the normal construction method, with the mill often forming part of it, as can be seen at Bolebrook Mill and Park Mill, Burwash. On occasions the mill was detached from its millpond, as at Boringwheel Mill, where a leat from the pond supplied water to the mill some 150 yards away. At Isfield Mill and Uckfield Mill the power of the River Uck was of sufficient strength to drive both mills without the need to pond the water, but this was not the common practice in the county.

TIDE MILLS

Around the coast of Britain a variation of the use of the millpond is found in a special type of watermill, known as a tide mill. The tide mill always formed part of the dam and more often had just one inlet so that when the tide came in water flowed into the pond, which eventually was impounded by closing the sluice gates. When the level of the downstream water had dropped sufficiently, the waterwheel sluices would be opened to allow the water onto the wheel. Owing to the exposed positions of most tide mills, a great number of them did not survive the ravages of the weather and few examples exist today. Eling Tidemill near Southampton is one of the best examples of its type and has been restored to working order. The former Bishopstone Tidemill, near Newhaven, was perhaps one of the biggest mills of its type in the country, with its three undershot waterwheels driving 16-pairs of stones.

LEFT: The overshot waterwheel complete but in a poor condition at Sheffield Mill in March 1935. (AS) BELOW: The low breastshot waterwheel at Horsebridge Mill in 1991. RIGHT: The new overshot waterwheel installed at Hellingly Mill in 1984.

17

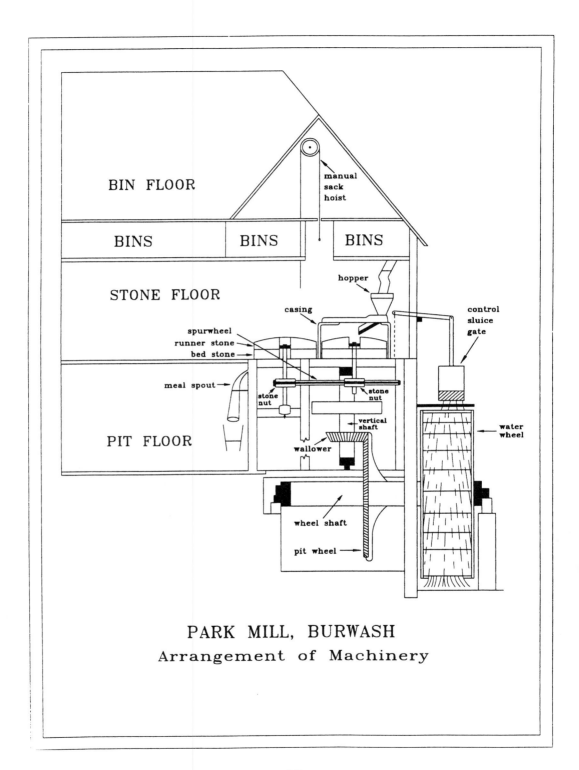

BIN FLOOR

BINS   BINS   BINS

manual
sack
hoist

hopper

STONE FLOOR

casing

control
sluice
gate

spurwheel
runner stone
bed stone

meal spout

stone
nut

stone
nut

vertical
shaft

water
wheel

PIT FLOOR

wallower

wheel shaft

pit wheel

PARK MILL, BURWASH
Arrangement of Machinery

18

A TYPICAL MILL

PARK MILL, BURWASH

Park Mill, Burwash is a Grade II listed watermill built in 1795 and is a brick-and-timber-framed three-storey building that stopped working at the turn of the century. The tiled roof is half-hipped at its northern end and, together with its pond, forms a most attractive rural scene. Following its restoration, the mill is now owned by the National Trust as it is part of 'Batemans', Rudyard Kipling's home from 1902 until 1936.

The power source of all watermills is derived from the waterwheel, which also drove all other ancillary machinery in the mill. The waterwheel at Park Mill was installed during the renovation of the mill but in width it bears little resemblance to its predecessor. Half of the former wheelpit is taken up by the turbine penstock and drive tube installed to power a generator to provide electricity to the nearby house in 1903. The waterwheel revolves on a wooden axle shaft which enters the mill and is connected to the pit wheel. As the perimeter of pit wheels was often set below the adjacent water level they were normally, as at Park Mill, constructed of cast iron.

It is inside the mill that the simple but ingenious machinery channels the water falling onto the wheel so as to rotate the millstones. The wooden upright shaft is contained to just within the pit floor, which again is unusual, and the great spur wheel attached to this shaft turns the three stone nut pinions. This vertical pinion is attached and rotates the top runner millstone. On the stone floor are 3-pairs of stones with a wooden casing enclosing the one working pair of stones.

Milling

When sacks of corn are received at the mill they are raised to the bin floor by means of a sack hoist, which is driven by pulleys from the waterwheel. The grain is stored in the meal bins set into the bin floor. A chute from the meal bin above pours the grain into the hopper above the stones and from here the corn is shaken into the 'eye', or centre, of the millstones. The bottom millstone (bedstone) is fixed to the floor, while the upper (runner) millstone revolves at about 100rpm. Both millstones have a set of grooves (furrows) cut into them. The grain is forced out through a gap between the millstones, where the action of the furrows crossing each other breaks the grain kernel and scrapes out the flour. The resultant meal (in other words, wholemeal flour) falls out of the periphery of the millstones and is swept down the meal spout to a sack on the pit floor below.

ABOVE: The front of the ornate Barcombe Mill in about 1900.
BELOW: Flooding at Shortbridge Mill in 1905. (BH)

THE POWER OF WATER

While corn milling was the principal industrial use of water power in East Sussex, there were other manufacturing processes such as oil, gunpowder, iron, paper and wool fulling that also relied on the use of water power.

GUNPOWDER

The gunpowder industry of East Sussex was first established at Peppering Eye, near Battle, in 1676. There were subsequently several other sites at Battle, Sedlescombe, Crowhurst and Brede, along with the shortlived site at Maresfield. Gunpowder mills were often located in spacious areas well away from populated villages or towns to minimise damage from explosions, but these sites are now open and treeless and, apart from the large site at Battle, little remains to indicate their former existence and the importance of the industry.

Gunpowder production relies heavily on the use of water power, and the sites at Battle, Brede and Maresfield used existing, and expansive, millponds that were first used for the Sussex iron industry.

The Sussex mills were renowned for the production of good quality sporting powder and the mills at Battle were granted special dispensation, under the 1772 Explosive Act, to continue the use of pestle mills, preferable for making this recreational powder.

The gunpowder industry in East Sussex ceased with the closure of Battle Mill in 1874, following representations from the residents of Battle, while some of the buildings were later used as a hotel.

PAPER

Unlike Surrey and Kent, the paper manufacturing industry in East Sussex was small and confined to just four sites on the River Ouse. The Ouse Navigation provided the means of transport of both the raw and finished product to and from the warehouses at Lewes.

The task of a paper mill was to pound rags into pulp suitable to make handmade paper. Paper was first produced in England using water power at the end of the 15th century, and it appears that most paper mills were located on the outskirts of towns or villages, where the quality and quantity of water were consistent and there was access to an important road or navigable water. Thus, four paper mills were established close to the River Ouse Navigation at Lewes, Isfield, Barcombe and Newick (although the purity of the water today does not readily associate itself with paper making).

21

The first recorded paper mill in East Sussex was at Barcombe, where, in 1706, a corn mill and paper mill were mentioned in a bankruptcy announcement. In 1802 a further mill was in operation at Lewes, in an area still known as 'The Pells', with the proprietors of the Lewes Paper Mill opening a new mill at Isfield in 1809. James Pim, a well-known papermaker, opened another mill near Newick (Sharp's Paper Mill) and ran it in conjunction with his similar business at Dean's Mill, Lindfield.

It is recorded that the Navigation provided the necessary ease of transport required and all four mills profited accordingly. Although the Navigation did not close until 1879, the paper mills had long ceased operating, with Sharp's Paper Mill the last to close.

FULLING

Examples of the water powered fulling mill no longer exist, although the external appearance and size of the mill would have been similar to the typical corn mill. Fulling was a process whereby woven cloth was scoured and cleaned to remove the natural oils and grease collected during its manufacture. The operation was traditionally manual, but it became apparent that the process could be accelerated by harnessing water to power the 'fulling stocks'. This involved a pair of wooden hammers, weighing approximately 1½ cwt being raised and dropped into a trough containing the cloth in a mixture of water and a cleaning agent, such as fuller's earth (which was deposited in vast amounts at Redhill in Surrey). The fulling process also ensured that the cloth became dense and opaque.

In East Sussex, fulling mills were few and only at four sites has this trade been recorded, although many earlier sites may have gone unrecorded. Both a fulling mill and a corn mill were recorded at Barcombe in the 16th century and other sites in the county could be found at Hempstead Mill, Shortbridge Mill and Sessingham — but, overall, this was a minor use of water power in East Sussex.

OIL

The oil mill at Barcombe was developed on such a large scale that in 1880 it was producing 80 tons of oil cake per week.

Oil milling was an ancient craft, mainly centred on the flat landscape of Eastern England, but the site by the River Ouse at Barcombe was also an important source of the product. Oil was used in the manufacture of soap and paint and for dressing raw wool before spinning, while oil cake was used for fuel, fertiliser and cattle food.

The production involved crushing the seeds in edge rolling millstones, after which they were placed in large linen bags and beaten by trip hammers. The initial source of power was the waterwheel, but in the case of the mill at Barcombe a 28hp beam engine was later fitted to power the 16 hydraulic presses.

The process of oil manufacture was smelly and unpopular with neighbouring inhabitants and most mills were situated in isolated positions. Barcombe Oil Mill was no exception when it was established following the opening of the River Ouse Navigation in 1793, and it prospered further when a small spur line was built to the nearby Lewes to Uckfield railway. On a much smaller scale, oil was also produced at Hempstead Mill near Uckfield, according to Gream's map of 1795, but only for a short period of time.

IRON

The history of the iron industry in the Weald has been fully documented in Ernest Straker's definitive book *Wealden Iron* and reference to this industry is only recorded when relevant to a subsequent water milling site.

Since Roman times, iron smelting has been carried out in the Weald, but it was a relatively small scale industry using iron ore that outcropped naturally. However, towards the end of the 15th century a revolution took place in the techniques of smelting iron with the introduction of the furnace. Into the furnace chamber projected several large bellows, which were compressed one after another by a rotating wheel driven by water power, ensuring that the mixed charcoal and ore burned not only quickly but at a much higher temperature. As the furnace was fed from the top it could work continuously if required. The operation of a furnace relied on a constant supply of water and, therefore, large millponds were constructed by the ironmasters. There are now few remaining artefacts from the iron industry apart from the large millponds, but even these are mostly dried up or exist in a much smaller form. In East Sussex there were 23 mill sites where mills were established following the cessation of the iron industry, no doubt due to the attraction of the expansive available water. Most were corn mills, although the sites at Battle, Brede and Maresfield were converted and used for gunpowder manufacture.

A view of the large Hempstead Mill in 1905. (BH)

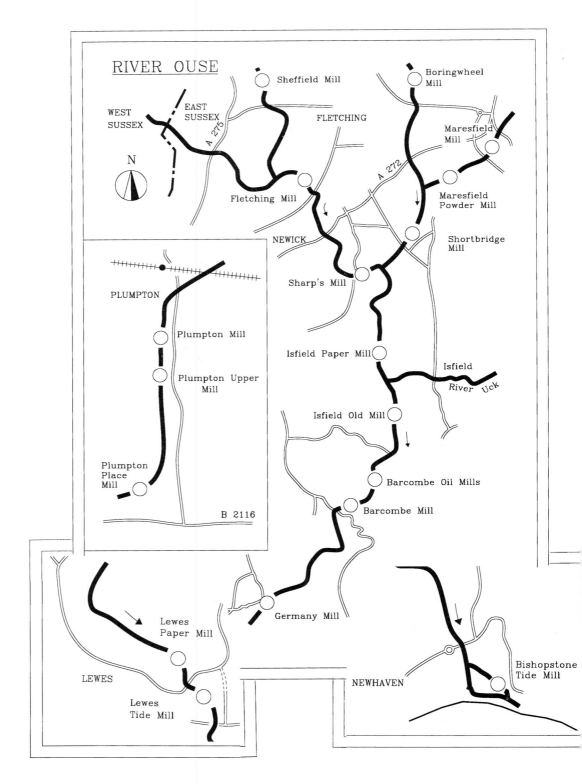

RIVER OUSE

Sheffield Mill

Boringwheel Mill

WEST SUSSEX

EAST SUSSEX

FLETCHING

Maresfield Mill

N

Fletching Mill

Maresfield Powder Mill

NEWICK

Shortbridge Mill

PLUMPTON

Sharp's Mill

Plumpton Mill

Isfield Paper Mill

Plumpton Upper Mill

Isfield

River Uck

Isfield Old Mill

Plumpton Place Mill

Barcombe Oil Mills

B 2116

Barcombe Mill

Lewes Paper Mill

Germany Mill

LEWES

NEWHAVEN

Bishopstone Tide Mill

Lewes Tide Mill

THE MILLS

RIVER OUSE

SHEFFIELD MILL *Danehill*
Tributary to River Ouse TQ 416 257 — East side of A275 one mile north of Sheffield Park.

Sheffield Mill lies at the bottom of a lane that branches eastwards off the Nutley to Maresfield road, and although this is only a small mill it has a large millpond that once supported an iron furnace.

It was common practice for a corn mill to be erected following the demise of the iron industry, but in this instance it was the other way round, for in 1197 a mill is mentioned here in a fine which made certain provisions in regard to 'the pond and watercourses at Sheffield'.

Both a furnace and a forge were in operation in 1546 but, although the forge carried on, the furnace had stopped by 1571 and during 1597-8 the corn mill was erected here on the disused furnace site which had used the main pond (the forge being alongside the nearby river itself).

This is a two-storey mill constructed in brick, timber and sandstone blocks, with a steep pitched roof of burnt tiles. The west side of the roof has a shallower pitch and was constructed to accommodate an extension to the mill in June 1911. Double doors lead directly into the mill and immediately it is apparent that the machinery is ancient and that the current millwrighting work being carried out under the direction of Jonathan Minns is desperately needed. The layshaft is wood and although the northern spur wheel has long gone, the southern wooden spur wheel, 5ft 6in in diameter, is of the clasp armed variety and again extremely old. All the machinery is contained on the ground floor with a wooden staging over the layshaft, supporting 2-pairs of millstones (one burr, one peak), which are contained in wooden octagonal cases.

The occupation of this mill during the 19th century was varied to say the least, i.e. 1828-37 James Dives, 1838-45 Thomas Ashby, 1866 Thomas Bingham, 1870 William Turner, 1882-1909 William Rayward (with his widow continuing until 1928). The mill and the detached listed mill house are delightfully situated in a wooded area and are both of some age. The north end of the mill house in particular appears medieval and is timber framed, infilled with sandstone and brick. A fire insurance plaque on the front of the house refers to John Cotter, the policy holder in 1791.

FLETCHING MILL *Fletching*
River Ouse TQ 423 229 — North of road half a mile southwest of Fletching.

Fletching Mill was two buildings in one, the original being the usual rectangular three-floor construction of brick and timber. Added to the roof, at its east end, was a four-storey wooden extension, square in shape, that towered above the original mill. This wooden addition, apart from housing the sack hoist and a wooden lucomb, had a flat roof. This unique extension was built by the Maryon-Wilson family, and tradition has it that the family could watch the progress of cricket matches at Sheffield Park from the roof of the mill, with a built-in trap door for access.

Ernest Straker, in his book *Wealden Iron*, refers to a forge at Fletching, which was in operation in 1574, but following the demise of the iron industry a corn mill was erected, with Charles Howard the tenant of the new mill. This mill was replaced by a later mill, demolished in 1950. Both mills took advantage of the nearby River Ouse Navigation and barges were often seen tied up at the wharf just upstream from the mill, until closure in 1879.

John Cotter had the mill in 1778, when there is also mention of a fulling mill on the site, and later the mill was owned by William Diplock, according to a sale auction notice, following his death, that appeared in the *Sussex Weekly Advertiser* of 11 August 1823. It appears that the mill was not sold, for Rebecca Diplock is recorded as the miller in trade directories of 1839, she being followed by Thomas Weston. The mill was using 3-pairs of stones, according to a tenancy advertisement that appeared in the *Sussex Advertiser* of February 1863. George Sparkes took over the mill until 1870 and he was followed by Joseph Martin, who stayed here until 1924. After his death, his widow carried on for a few years but, soon after, Tidy & Sons were in control, although the mill was not being worked by water power.

In 1940 the buildings were requisitioned by the War Office and soldiers were billeted in the mill itself. During this period the fabric of the mill suffered considerable damage. After the war the mill carried on, but only on an infrequent basis. An inspection of the mill in May 1946 declared that the 14ft 10in diameter breastshot waterwheel was still intact but the mill was derelict with the windows and doors boarded up and the pit gearing removed. Alas, in 1950 this most interesting watermill was pulled down and, as a further insult, the old humpback bridge in front of the mill was rebuilt.

Nothing now remains of Fletching Mill and the area where the mill formerly stood has been grassed over. Approximately 20,000 bricks from the mill were used locally, in addition to the hardcore which was used to repair the roads. Although there appears to be traces of the millrace, it is now virtually impossible to picture the mill at this site. Next to the site on the opposite side of the Ouse is the mill house, which is prone to flooding, according to the owner. Opposite the mill house is a farm building and on the top floor, amongst a heap of rusting ironwork, was found what appeared to be a wooden spar. Closer inspection revealed it to be a wooden casting pattern in the shape of an upright shaft. Under the threat of disposal, the pattern was removed for safe keeping to Ifield watermill.

SHARP'S PAPER MILL *Newick*
River Ouse TQ 440 208 — By the Piltdown to Barcombe Cross Road.

Sharp's Paper Mill was established between 1813 and 1816, when a property called 'Sharp's' was purchased by James Pim, a well-known papermaker, who was also running Dean's Paper Mill at Lindfield. Pim's decision to build a paper mill here may have been influenced by the success of the two other paper mills further downstream at Isfield and Lewes.

Pim was the only occupier of the mill, and in the sale particulars that appeared in the *Sussex Advertiser* of 6 September 1853 a full and comprehensive description of the paper mill was given:

'To be sold by auction at the White Hart, Lewes, on the 13th September, 1853, by direction of the proprietor Mr James Pim. All that valuable property known as Sharp's Paper Mill, situated at Sharp's Bridge, near Piltdown, consisting of a stone, brick and timber built tile healed Mill House 68ft by 33ft, containing machine, rag store, and drying rooms: a brick-built tile healed Machine House, 30ft by 21ft, and a stone built slate healed building attached to ditto, a brick and stone built healed Engine House 30ft by 27ft, a range of brick and stone built slate and tile healed cottage residences, in seven tenements, general bakehouse, a new brick built tile healed Store Room 18ft by 17ft, a good stable for four horses, well situated and adjoining the wharf. This is an excellent opportunity for transforming the present mill into oil or corn mills. There is every reason to suppose that a railway will shortly be formed from Lewes to Tunbridge Wells. The above is Copyhold of the Manor of Barcombe subject to a quit rent of 1s 8d, a heriot of best beast on death or surrender, but if the vendor has not a beast then in a fine of only 20s and two years quit rent of 1s 8d.'

It can be deduced from the above that paper making had already ceased here, but it seems that no buyer was found for the site. Pim also relinquished his control of his other paper mill at Lindfield at the same time.

This was only a small paper mill, with one engine, and at the time was just one of three such mills left in Sussex, the others being at Iping and West Ashling, according to the Parliamentary Returns of 1851.

There does not appear to be a trace left of the mill, but the 1874 Ordnance Survey 25in map shows a leat branching off the main river just downstream of the road bridge before rejoining it by Sharp's Bridge Lock. On this leat are signs of ponding, but little exists to shows its exact position. A site inspection, however, revealed the site of the mill just to the north-west of Sharp's Bridge Lock. Here are to be found some discarded sandstone blocks together with a drop in ground level at the end of a filled in, but still discernable, mill leat that ran parallel with the main river.

Sharp's Paper Mill has vanished into history, but by the road bridge that connects Isfield with Piltdown were four properties named 'Sharp's Cottages', which were of an age commensurate with that of the paper mill. Modern houses now occupy this site but just to the north is 'Sharp's Bridge House', which is probably the property 'Sharp's' purchased by James Pim in 1813.

BORINGWHEEL MILL *Nutley*
Tributary to River Ouse TQ 456 265 — North side of Cackle Street.

This mill is to be found on the north side of Cackle Street, a small lane branching off the A22 just south of Nutley. The mill now forms part of a group of farm buildings and, outwardly, has the appearance of a wooden shed.

The site was originally connected with the iron industry, as Ernest Straker in his book *Wealden Iron* states that a 'Boringwheel pond' was mentioned in the Parliamentary Surveys of the Ashdown Forest for 1658. The name, together with local tradition, suggests that cannon may have been bored here as late as the 1770s. The cannons were cast hollow and then reamed out by a special tool powered by water power, and the size of the existing millpond would seem to confirm its association with the iron industry.

There is a wooden lean-to on the south side of the mill, which formerly housed a small steam or oil engine. It was originally a 2-pair mill, although one position has been boarded over, and most of the machinery remains in place. The wooden waterwheel, approximately 12ft by 4ft and overshot, has long gone, with the iron wheel axle shaft protruding out of an empty wheelpit with its two twin water feed pipes now redundant. The drive machinery is predominantly iron, with the wooden upright shaft the exception. The pit machinery is contained within a wooden cupboard and is arranged in the standard layout, with a 9ft pit wheel and a 9ft 6in spur wheel. In its latter working days only 1-pair of stones was used and the stone nut and jack ring remain. Along with the bedstone on the stone floor above is the crown wheel, 4ft 8in in diameter. This drove ancillary shafting from both sides, one of which operated the sack hoist. The predominantly iron machinery dates back to the second half of the 19th century, a time when many mills made similar modifications. The 1840 Tithe Map Apportionment records that Thomas Avery was the occupier here, while in 1866 Allen Avery was described as a miller and farmer of Boringwheel Mill. In 1895 Frank Walden, the miller, was described as a baker, corn and coal merchant. However, later on in that year he is described as bankrupt! Over the next 20 years a succession of millers occupied the mill, i.e. 1899 James Brook, 1907 Thomas Kent, 1909 Sidney Simmons, 1913 Alfred Allitt. After 1915 all trade directory entries relating to this mill cease, and little other information exists.

Unusually, the mill was some distance from its millpond, from which a leat was taken off the south-east corner. The water then ran in an open channel past the mill house to the wheelpit through two iron pipes. At the back of the mill house are signs of a dried-up watercourse and it is surmised that a stream, rising in Ashdown Forest and running southwest towards the mill, may have been used to supplement the water supply here.

Surprisingly, even though Boringwheel Mill ceased operating about 80 years ago, the mill building and its machinery have survived. Perhaps its use as a store room for the nearby mill house saved it from going the way of so many other watermills in the country.

MARESFIELD MILL *Maresfield*

Tributary to River Ouse TQ 470 236 — Stood adjacent to the old A22 south of village.

On 29 June 1877, Maresfield Mill burnt down, according to a report that appeared in the *Sussex Advertiser* on 3 July that year:

'On Thursday morning (June 29) a very destructive fire occurred on the mill premises of Mr John Hill, Maresfield, when the mill house was also damaged. A workman noticed a volume of smoke coming from the mill when going to work at 4 o'clock in the morning and aroused Mr Hill. The Uckfield Volunteer Fire Brigade was sent for and was soon on the spot, but too late to save the mill which, consisting of a brick base and weatherboarding, was powerless to resist the flames. Shortly after 5 o'clock the whole structure fell with a crash. The damage to Mr Hill is estimated at £2,000 at least. The mill belonged to Lady Shelley, of Maresfield Park.

'Mr Hill has been a resident of the property for 47 years. For a very long period he was manager of the mill for the late Sir John Villiers Shelley and has been the occupying tenant during the last 19 years. The account of the fire speaks of a steam engine boiler on the premises which was not in regular use.'

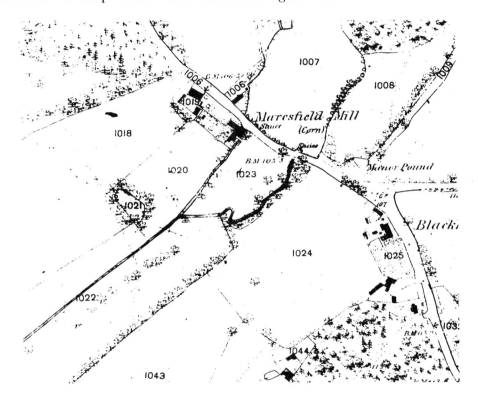

Apparently, the mill was in good working order when the fire broke out and large stocks of corn were destroyed, but the damage to the mill house was less serious. The fire ended corn milling at the site and in January 1878 the remaining machinery, not damaged by the fire, was advertised for sale. It included an overshot waterwheel 20ft in diameter and 4ft wide. The newspaper account of the fire refers to John Hill as the manager, while the 1840 Tithe Map Apportionment refers to Thomas Dray as the occupier. He was probably employed by Hill. As the mill was worked by a 20ft diameter waterwheel, it must have been a fairly substantial mill, working at least 3-pairs of millstones. According to a trade directory published in 1866, the mill had become the 'Maresfield Water & Steam Mills' but little further is known about this venture.

The mill house, much altered (or possibly rebuilt since the fire), is now the only indication of the mill's existence, as the millpond — on the opposite side of the road — disappeared during major road improvements.

MARESFIELD POWDER MILL *Maresfield*

Tributary to River Ouse TQ 460 228 — Approximately one mile southwest of the village.

Before the gunpowder mills were established here, the site was used as a furnace for the iron industry (it closed down in 1812). John Villiers Shelley purchased the land in 1848-9 and applied for and was granted a licence to erect powder mills here. The *Sussex Advertiser* of 8 June 1850 published the following announcement:

'Maresfield. On arrival here, on Tuesday last, of the news that Mr J. Villiers Shelley of Maresfield Park had been successful in his application at the Sessions for a licence for his projected Powder Mills, considerable rejoicing was evinced by our inhabitants, and the bells were put into requisition to send forth a merry peal in token of the joyful intelligence.'

The Maresfield Patent Gunpowder Company used a new method to produce the powder. All three ingredients were boiled together in a vacuum, but apparently with little success, and after the credibility of the management was questioned the company was made bankrupt in 1859. There is no doubt that steam power was predominantly used here, but some water power would also have been used.

The gunpowder mill continued production under different ownership until a massive explosion took place, as the *Sussex Advertiser* graphically recorded. Apparently, a man sheltering from the rain, after lighting his pipe, threw the match down in a corner of the room where there was loose gunpowder strewn about. The result was a massive explosion, which blew the roof of the mill off, fortunately without loss of life. After this newspaper report all references to the powder mill cease.

A discarded incorporating millstone, lying near to the millpond, is the only surviving relic from the industry, as the vast pond and the immediate surrounding area have been extensively landscaped over the years. The modern dwelling, known as 'Mill Cottage', is new and replaced an earlier structure connected with the gunpowder industry.

The site was originally reached by a trackway that connected directly with the village, but following construction of the A22 Maresfield bypass, a shortened vehicular access can be made from the new road, while a well-signposted public footpath passes through the site.

SHORTBRIDGE MILL *Shortbridge*

Tributary to River Ouse TQ 451 214 — Adjacent to unclassified road one mile west of Uckfield.

Shortbridge Mill is a listed three-storey redbrick building that has been converted into a private residence of some style, complete with its idyllic millpond. The site is dominated by a very tall chimney stack, which testifies to the use of steam power here.

The first reference to a corn mill appeared in 1803, when John Packham, the miller, was referred to in the Defence Schedules of that year. In 1871 this mill was later replaced by the present structure, which continued working through to the 1930s.

When the River Ouse Navigation was extended to Fletching in 1793 the existing mill had its own canal branch, complete with a large wharf and store house. This short length of canal branched off the main Navigation at a point just to the north of Sharp's Bridge Lock. Despite the direct canal access to Lewes, the mill survived the closure of the Ouse Navigation in 1879, but the Uckfield railway no doubt provided an alternative means of transport.

The water supply for the mill was provided by a cut from Maresfield Lake, but during the summer months the ailing water supply was eventually supplemented by the introduction of a beam engine and boiler house — the engine reputedly coming from Maresfield Powder Mills.

From at least 1803 John Packham, a member of the well-known milling family, was in control, with his widow carrying on from 1833. She was succeeded by a Mr Fleet, with George Kenward taking over soon after. He was replaced by John and then Peter Hill, the latter being the miller during the construction of the new mill. After Hill, William Wright (1881-97) and William Fairhall (1897-1909) were in occupation and, finally, the last occupiers were the Kenward Bros. After closure the mill appeared ripe for preservation for, in 1947, the mill lay complete and seemingly in no danger. However, all of the internal machinery was then cleared, most being sold for scrap with the fate of the beam engine unknown.

Shortbridge Mill is an attractive brick-built building and, apart from the boiler house chimney, the only other external feature to be seen is the framework of the pitchback waterwheel, along with the pentrough. The waterwheel is one of the few examples of S. Burgess of Lewes (his name and the date of 1871 are inscribed upon it). It is iron, 9ft in diameter and 8ft 6in wide, and developed 10hp. Although originally an overshot wheel, it was converted to a pitchback wheel later. This was possible because the iron pentrough and starter gate, manufactured by Avery's of Lewes, was in front of the waterwheel and brought water from the millpond, passed by the wheel and fed it backwards towards it, a most unusual arrangement.

Shortbridge Mill stands proudly by the side of a road that connects Isfield with Piltdown and, although it only operated for a relatively short period, it certainly was an important East Sussex mill.

ISFIELD OLD MILL *Isfield*
River Ouse TQ 444 173 — Southwest of the village centre.

This is probably an ancient mill site, though its history is shrouded in mystery. There is a reference to an 'Old Mill', without the usual map symbol, on Greenwood's map of 1823, but there is no mention in the reliable Tithe Apportionment of 1840.

The 1874 Ordnance Survey 25in map depicts the site of the mill immediately to the west of 'Old Mill Farm'. A leat was cut from the Ouse upstream of 'Old Mill Bridge', which then passed under the track leading to the bridge, where the outline of a pond is shown. The tail race then rejoined the river further downstream.

It is probable that the mill disappeared during the latter years of the 18th century, when the new Isfield Mill was built.

ISFIELD PAPER MILL *Isfield*
River Ouse TQ 440 185 — One mile northwest of the village centre.

When the River Ouse was made navigable to Isfield in 1793, a lock was constructed to the west of Isfield Place. The proprietors of the Navigation then offered for sale, in October 1795, two acres of land next to Isfield Lock, as a desirable location for a mill.

The land was purchased by Molineux and Johnston, who later operated a large paper mill at The Pells in Lewes. The opening of the Isfield Mill was celebrated in some style according to an article that appeared in the *Sussex Weekly Advertiser* in July 1809. The mill was described as being very powerful and manufacturing white paper.

The Excise Lists of 1816 numbered the mill as 391, worked by Messrs Molineux and Johnston. A description of the mill in 1827 stated that it was a large and handsome paper mill on the bank of the river. Nonetheless, the mills at Isfield and Lewes were advertised for sale in the *Sussex Advertiser* of October 1855:

'Paper Mills, Lewes and Isfield. Messrs Grafter will sell by auction at Carraways Coffee House, Change Alley, Cornhill, London on the 9 October 1855. The spacious mills and other property, comprising the substantial and well arranged mill and appendages, situated close to the town of Lewes. Also, the spacious and convenient mill situated at Isfield, only five miles from Lewes, with a foreman's house and nine cottages. Both mills possess ample water power, also spring water, steam engine fixtures and fittings, and were formerly used for the manufacture of paper on an extensive scale. Being both on the River Ouse Navigation, they could conveniently be adapted to other purposes.'

It appears that both mills remained unsold and the arrival of the railway through Isfield in 1858 did not help the situation. The *Sussex Advertiser* of 15 September 1857 recorded the final demise of Isfield Paper Mill:

'To be sold by auction on the premises at Isfield Paper Mill on 28 September 1857. The whole of the materials of the Foreman's cottage, nine cottages, bricks, together with the valuable stone of the water courses of the late Paper Mill, two large cast iron waterwheels etc.'

So ended a profitable yet brief industry by the banks of the River Ouse Navigation. The 1874 Ordnance Survey 25in map shows signs of ponding just to the west of the disused lock, but little else to indicate the exact site of the mill, let alone traces of the nine cottages!

This is now an area of peaceful tranquillity, far removed from the noise and waste of the paper mill.

PLUMPTON PLACE MILL *Plumpton*
Tributary to River Ouse TQ 361 135 — West side of Plumpton Lane, south of village.

This mill is the southernmost of the three watermills at Plumpton and is rather an undistinguished building set in an idyllic location. The mill is brick-and-timbered and was completely gutted and converted into a house, with the iron and wooden-paddled 20ft diameter overshot waterwheel being removed in 1927, when a Mr Pickard bought the mill. According to the *Sussex Weekly Advertiser* of 8 February 1802, the mill was erected by Lord Pelham, the Earl of Chichester, for the benefit of the poor and the industrious, while a week later, the same newspaper reported that the miller was not permitted to take toll. The mill took its name from the nearby Plumpton Place, a half-timbered moated house that dates back to 1568.

A. J. Eldridge was the recorded occupier in 1841, he in turn being succeeded by John Mansbridge in 1848 until he left in 1866. James Harris and his son James ran the mill until 1895, after which the mill ceased milling commercially. Records indicate that the mill continued running until 1916, but this was only on a casual basis. After World War I, Mr Edward Hudson purchased Plumpton Place and restored the house under the guidance of Sir Edwin Lutyens.

Following a change of estate ownership in the 1980s, a new waterwheel was installed for aesthetic reasons. The iron overshot waterwheel is inscribed 'Cast at the Brighton Engineerium JM 1984 PT' and is 7ft 6in in diameter by 5ft 3in wide, but it does look rather out of place in the large wheelpit. There was never a water shortage at this site as there are three large ponds between the mill and Plumpton Place, the highest of which is spring fed from the escarpment of the South Downs.

PLUMPTON UPPER MILL *Plumpton*
Tributary to River Ouse TQ 363 147 — West side of Plumpton Lane, south of village.

This is the middle of the three watermills at Plumpton and is by far the smallest, with the appearance of a small outbuilding when viewed from the causeway that branches westwards off Plumpton Lane.

The present 'Upper Mill' was rebuilt as a corn mill in 1740 and was in joint ownership with Plumpton Mill in 1780, and probably earlier. A reference to both mills under one ownership is made in the Tithe Apportionment of 1842 and the partnership continued until the closure of both mills.

Previously, this site held a fulling mill — as confirmed by the adjacent field to the west, called Fulling Mill Field.

Upper Mill has an exquisite waterwheel that has been preserved and repaired by the present owners. It is an iron overshot wheel 11ft in diameter by 4ft 10in wide and is inscribed 'A. SHAW LEWES 1886', while the pentrough carries the inscription 'Bishop and Wells'. There is a double iron pipefeed to the wheel which is so balanced that it can be turned with just one finger! Access to the pit floor is at ground level at the front of the mill and the existing iron pit machinery is of a date comparable with that of the waterwheel. Access to the stone floor is by way of steps at the side of the mill. Most of the machinery was removed earlier this century when the stone floor and bin floor were used as a workshop and studio.

The Homewood family occupied both mills until 1840, after which they were taken over by John Beard. The mills were advertised for sale in June 1848 but, according to the *Sussex Advertiser*, nothing came of this. Beard was apparently retiring, but four years later the *London Gazette* recorded him as an insolvent debtor. In 1850 his son Richard Beard took over and ran both mills until 1905, after which the mill was leased to Richard Bodle, who advertised the mills under the 'Plumpton Milling Co'. Later, in 1911, the mills were leased to Messrs Caffyn, Hollis & Hollis and, according to *Kelly's* trade directory of 1922, Henry Hollis was the sole occupier. After this date all references cease.

Although this is a small building, it was referred to as a 'Flour Mill' on the 1873 Ordnance Survey 25in map, at a time when most mills were producing just provender feed. Upper Mill is a pleasant-looking buiding, set into the pond embankment and built of red brick to two floors, with weatherboarded gabled ends under a tiled mansard roof — all kept in good order. The tail race from the wheel has been piped, and broken burr millstones have been set into the base of the embankment next to the mill. The once large millpond, known as the 'Reed Pond', is now overgrown but even in summer water pours out over the overflow weir. This is a most attractive site, with the mill house and natural gardens forming a pleasant scene, though the mill is on strictly private property.

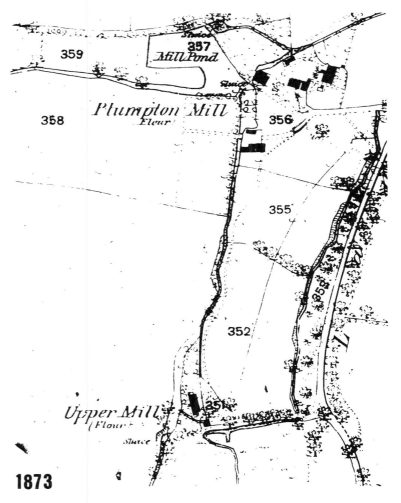

1873

PLUMPTON MILL *Plumpton*

Tributary to River Ouse TQ 363 150 — West side of Plumpton Lane, south of village.

Plumpton Mill was the largest of the three watermills located on a small tributary of the River Ouse, to the south of the village, and worked in conjunction with the Upper Mill. The present mill possibly dates from the beginning of the 19th century, but could be the mill referred to when Francis Homewood was the occupier in 1780. In the reliable 1803 Defence Schedule, it was the only mill mentioned at Plumpton — but Homewood claimed that owing to the failure of the water at the time he could not ascertain any particulars concerning output in times of war.

The 1842 Tithe Map Apportionment refers to Joseph Beard as the owner and occupier, while later the mill continued to work in conjunction with the Upper Mill, with the millers the same.

Plumpton Mill is an attractive building, with brick to the first floor and white weatherboarding above, under a double mansard half-hipped roof. The 12ft diameter

34

by 5ft 6in wide iron overshot waterwheel is in exceptional condition, with the maker's name 'A SHAW 1892' inscribed four times on the outer rim of the wheel, which is set on a hollow iron axle shaft. The pentrough starter box, made at the same foundry, bears the date 1889. Inside the mill the machinery is set out in a standard layout, apart from a drive pinion from a bevel shaft, below the spur wheel, which once drove a generator. A bricked-up axle hole in the wheelpit inner wall indicates the previous position of a smaller waterwheel here, probably the original, before it was replaced in 1892, with the original iron water feed pipes extended to cater for the larger diameter wheel. The mill was last mentioned in a directory entry of 1922, but was restarted and was working briefly some years ago. The part of the building housing the waterwheel and the pit machinery is the original mill, but at a later date the mill was extended eastwards under a matching, but smaller, tiled mansard roof. The mill is set into the side of a large pond embankment and access is gained to the top floor from the adjacent track across the causeway. The water supply of the millpond is from a separate tributary to that which feeds the millpond at the Upper Mill, although there is an old watercourse between the two mills, which is presently dry. At the time of the authors' visit (1995), the millpond was completely dried up, but over the years the mill and house have been regularly flooded and the sluice is deliberately left open at times.

This is another attractive site on private property but, although the present owners keep the mill in good condition, it will probably never produce flour again.

BARCOMBE OIL MILL *Barcombe*
River Ouse TQ 438 158 — One mile east of Barcombe Cross south of Anchor Lane.

The first reference to a mill here is when Thomas Rickman insured the contents of his brick-built oil mill on the site. One of the principal attractions of the location was the neighbouring River Ouse Navigation, which has opened for commercial traffic in 1793.

Although always referred to as 'Barcombe Oil Mill', this conceals the fact that from the beginning a corn mill was incorporated here, as later confirmed in a trade directory entry of 1839 when both industries are indicated. Details of both trades are given in the sale notice that appeared in the *Sussex Advertiser* of 25 April 1848:

'To be sold by auction on May 16, 1848, at the Star Inn, Lewes. The celebrated Freehold Oil Mills, fitted with two breast wheels, two pairs of large vertical grinding stones, 15 presses with stoves, and two pairs of rollers; also four pairs of corn mill French stones, double action high pressure steam engine, extensive warehouse, the oil cisterns to hold 70 tons of oil, together with a substantial warehouse with three floors situated in the town of Lewes on the River Ouse.'

Disaster struck on 6 June 1854 when the mill caught fire, causing between £7,000 and £8,000 worth of damage. According to a newspaper report, large patches of burning oil floated downstream and threatened the nearby Barcombe Mill. R. H. Billiter, the owner of the mill, placed an article in the *Sussex Advertiser* soon after the fire to announce that he was still able to supply genuine linseed cake at £10 10s a ton. He also stated that he had every reason to believe that the mill destroyed by the fire would be at work again shortly. The mill was for sale in June 1880 on instructions of the executors of the late R. H. Billiter, and the sale advertisement gives a clear indication of the contents of the oil mill. The *Sussex Advertiser* carried the following notice:

'Lot 1. The Oil and Upper Flour Mill, on the River Ouse, at Barcombe. A large and substantial building 120 feet by 64 feet; engine house 36 feet by 27 feet, a detached oil store 45 feet square, gas house, cottage, stabling and other buildings. The mills are driven by two breast waterwheels (one iron and one wood) and a large 28hp beam steam engine capable of working 80 tons of oil cake and about 200 quarters of wheat per week. They are arranged throughout with spacious stores and fitted with the best machinery. In the oil mill there are two sets of double pumps, 16 hydraulic presses with 10in rams, one pair of granite and one pair of York stones: and in the flour mill, four pairs of french wheat stones. The mills are in the occupation of Messrs William Tickner & Co.'

The freehold was purchased by H. Drewitt & Son, but this venture soon failed, while Edward Kenward was the occupier from 1905 until 1909 (though he was only using the corn mill). The reason that the oil mill continued for so long was due to the short spur line that connected with the Lewes to Uckfield railway. As an alternative to the canal transport, the horse and cart was regularly used and, according to a 19th-century report, the roads leading from the mill were covered with oil drips.

There are no futher references to the mill after 1911, although it is possible that the corn mill carried on working until the mill closed down and was demolished in about 1917. Little remains to indicate the exact site of the mill apart from the overgrown sluice gate and a pile of discarded edge runners stones. A small cottage, possible once belonging to the lock-keeper remains, and in the summer this must be a delightful location.

BARCOMBE MILL *Barcombe*
River Ouse TQ 423 149 — Just north of Barcombe Mills Road.

Early references to this ancient mill site are sparse and it is not until the 16th century that mention is made. It is recorded that Thomas Erith held a fulling mill here, but it was possible that the corn mill was here also. Later, in 1706, there was a combined corn and paper mill here, according to details recorded in a bankruptcy sale.

The mill site began to develop in the 1790s when the Ouse was made navigable from Lewes to Cuckfield. William Jessop, the eminent canal engineer, carried out the investigative work and, following his recommendations, the Navigation was built and opened for commercial traffic in 1793. The proprietors of this and the nearby Barcombe Oil Mill were Thomas Rickman & Son, and in this respect they had taken up a lease on a warehouse at the Cliffe at Lewes. The opening of the Navigation eased the transfer of flour and produce to Lewes and to villages futher upstream. As with its neighbouring mill, Richard Billiter was also the owner here by 1855 and he, like Thomas Rickman before him, rented warehouse premises at Lewes. In 1858 the Lewes to Uckfield railway opened, revolutionising the commercial transport of materials and spelling the end of the Navigation, and a railway siding was constructed from the mill to Barcombe Mills Station. A new and much larger mill was erected here in 1870 on the south side of the road bridge, built mainly of pitch pine with a semi-classic facade. It had four floors and was powered by two enclosed waterwheels. It was capable of producing 500 to 600 sacks of flour per week. Following the sale of the mill in 1879 the mill was taken over by William Catt & Sons, who were operating the massive

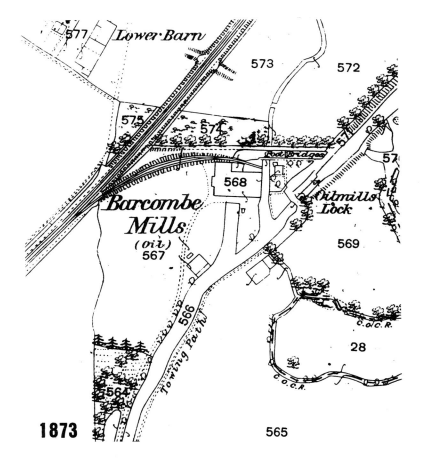

1873

Bishopstone Tide Mill south of Newhaven. Later, in 1894, when John Catt was the owner, a Turner five-sack roller mill was installed. Motive power for the roller plant was provided by a 60hp compound engine, while a 'Little Giant' turbine was installed to drive the remaining 3-pairs of millstones.

By 1903, the mill was in the occupation of William Wilmshurst, who continued until the closure of the mill in 1918, according to a trade directory entry of that year.

After the mill had lain derelict, the buildings were leased in 1931 for the manufacture of buttons, but without using water power. Nuts were imported from Italy and machinery was installed to slice them into coat buttons.

In March 1939 the mill caught fire and quickly burnt to the ground. Today there is only a grass mound, which houses an atmospheric syphon that forces water downstream as necessary. The old road bridge, where the miller extracted toll rights, remains — but the neighbouring small brick building had no connection with the mill (it once housed pumping equipment for the lake at Barcombe House). Two peak millstones lie discarded by the river, while four separate waterways — including the remains of the old canal — pass through the site, showing how the water was controlled for use by one of the largest watermills in East Sussex.

GERMANY MILL *Hamsey*

River Ouse TQ 412 123 — Adjacent to farm track leading to Hamsey Church.

The search for the curiously named Germany Mill is not easy, as it stands among farm buildings that have no apparent connection with its past.

The village of Hamsey is now nothing more than a scattering of houses. The original village, long since disappeared, lay around the church, but the present village is situated in the middle of a flat and open area on the flood plains to the north of Lewes. It once possessed a windmill as well. The area is criss-crossed by dykes, which include the River Ouse Navigation.

Germany Mill was built in 1744, according to a rather decayed stone tablet fixed above the entrance door. It is a three-storey brick and flint building with wooden gables under a tiled roof. It is now completely devoid of any milling machinery and now houses modern grain-drying equipment. There is no water supply to the site, probably due to the construction of the adjacent Navigation in 1793, which drastically altered the position of the old River Ouse and cut off the water supply to the mill.

The track from Offham leads to the site, passing through Hamseyplace Farm, and ends abruptly at Hamsey Church, which dates back to Norman times. The immediate surrounding area includes a disused railway line and further flood prevention earthworks. There appears to be a dearth of historical references to the mill and its past is now shrouded in mystery.

LEWES PAPER MILL *Lewes*

Papermill Cut — River Ouse TQ 412 123 — Adjacent to the River Ouse at 'The Pells'.

The paper mills at Lewes and Isfield were linked by common ownership. A report in the *Sussex Chronicle* of February 1802 states that the paper mill at Lewes was in a state of readiness. The proprietors Messrs Molineux, Johnston & Lee were to manufacture thick and thin quality writing paper and the report went on to say that a few 'steady' women were required to work in the mill. The paper mill was demolished in about 1825 and later, in 1860, a large steam flour mill was constructed, according to a report that appeared in the *Sussex Advertiser* in October of that year. It appears that the flour mill operated only for a few years, for the utensils of the steam mill were advertised for sale in June 1868.

The site of the paper mill is located to the west of an industrial estate at 'The Pells' in what is now an area of waste ground to the south of the River Ouse. There are still traces of 'Papermill Cut', which provided the water power to the mill, although following the construction of the flood prevention embankments there is no outlet for this dried-up watercourse. This 'cut' was taken off the main river at Hamsey, a mile upstream, and ran parallel with the River Ouse in order to generate a sufficient head of water at the mill site. Thus, Lewes Paper Mill has become just another statistic to be added to the ever growing list of watermill sites in the county.

LEWES TIDE MILL *Lewes*

River Ouse TQ 420 107 — South of Lewes Bridge beside the River Ouse.

Mention is made on Budgeon's map of 1724 to a tide mill at Lewes, but there are no references to it before or after this date.

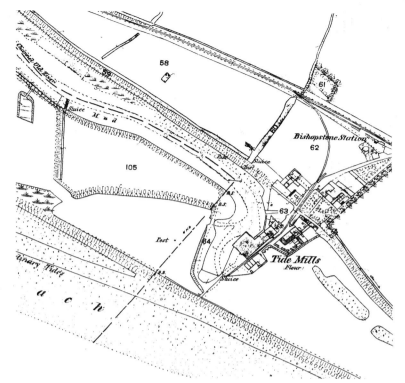

The area to the immediate south of the old Lewes Bridge consists of warehouses associated with the various commercial concerns on the west bank of the River Ouse. Running through this area is the Winterbourne Stream, which flows into the main river. In the winter it is just possible to make out artificial embankments here that were possibly connected with it, but these few remains are not definite enough to identify positively the former site of Lewes Tide Mill.

BISHOPSTONE TIDE MILL *Bishopstone*
River Ouse TQ 459 002 — On the foreshore southeast of Newhaven.

Bishopstone Tide Mill was extraordinary in that, apart from being the largest watermill in Sussex, a whole community — including workers' houses and a school — formed part of this isolated site. Thomas Pelham, Duke of Newcastle, obtained an Act of Parliament to use the foreshore of his land at Bishopstone and harness the tides for a proposed tide mill. The mill erected in 1788 was of a type and size commonly found at the time, but Pelham died before it was completed and in 1791 it was advertised for sale, according to the *Sussex Weekly Advertiser*. Apparently, the mill contained 5-pairs of stones and was capable of grinding 130 quarters of wheat per week.

Its prominent and exposed position caused problems over the years, especially with flooding. In 1792 the *Sussex Weekly Advertiser* reported that during a great storm considerable quantities of wheat and flour were destroyed. Following the sale of the mill the new owner, Thomas Barton, set about improving the efficiency of the site and erected a large three-storey mill containing 16-pairs of stone that could produce 1,500 sacks of flour per week! Just before the turn of the century, Barton was in partnership with Edmund Catt, but this arrangement was dissolved (according to the *London Gazette*) in 1801. Edmund Catt was then joined by his cousin William, the latter in turn dissolving the partnership in 1807. William Catt came from a family of millers and farmers from the Buxted and Robertsbridge areas and, being an astute businessman, developed a highly profitable concern at Bishopstone. Storm damage appeared to be a common occurence here. One of the most violent storms took place in 1820, when the mill building itself was damaged and part of the mill dam was washed away, according to the *Sussex Weekly Advertiser*.

William Catt died in March 1853, leaving his sons to carry on the business, but soon after the mill started gradually to decline, with the inclement weather a major factor. The mill did, however, continue in a limited capacity until March 1883, when a combination of another violent storm together with the requirements for an improved harbour at Newhaven, caused the mill to stop work altogether, as *The Miller* reported:

'The Tide Mills at Bishopstone, Sussex, having been closed owing to requirements of the Harbour works at Newhaven, the standing and going machinery and gear at the mill are now offered for sale by private tender. The whole is in complete working order, the mills having been in full operation up to March 25th last. The plant includes various machines, 12 pairs of french stones 4ft 6in diameter driving with the sun. Four pairs of french stones 4ft 6in diameter driving against the sun.'

Bishopstone Tide Mill was no ordinary mill site, as (according to the census returns of 1851) 60 men were employed here, the majority of whom lived on site with their families. Catt built workers' cottages and even a school and it became a vibrant community, although conditions were rather primitive. Although Catt worked his employees hard, they came to respect his authority and the care he took of their dependents. A later development at the site was the introduction of a spur to the Newhaven-Seaford railway line. This siding ran between the cottages and up to the mill and enabled vast quantities of flour to be carried into Newhaven for distribution, especially by sea to London.

A tide mill works simply on water being released from the storage ponds when the tide is on the ebb, with the outgoing water turning the waterwheels. At Bishopstone there were three undershot waterwheels in operation, all approximately 15ft in diameter, together with two large storage ponds and several other small side lagoons. William Catt erected a windmill on the roof of the mill and used this to power a sack hoist in the mill below. A hundred years of milling ended when the mill closed down in 1883, but this was not the end of occupancy here, as fishermen lived in the cottages vacated by the mill workers and, until demolition in 1901, the mill was used as a bonded warehouse for the Café Royal in London. Subsequently, the site was used as a holiday base, with beach huts and old railway carriages, but during World War I an extensive seaplane base was established and a large hangar erected. Taking off or landing must have been rather hazardous, considering the windy conditions that seem to prevail here most of the time. After the war riding stables occupied the site, with the old mill house being used for accommodation, while later, in 1930, the Chailey Heritage Beach hospital was built in the village. At the outbreak of World War II the gently sloping shingle beach was deemed a suitable landing place for enemy forces and all the residents were given 24 hours' notice to leave. After the threat of invasion subsided the derelict buildings were used by the Army as a training area for street fighting, with the remaining buildings being demolished as part of an exercise.

There is little evidence to be seen of the former mill site apart from three large culverts, which once contained the waterwheels, and some shingle walls, which had no connection with the mill. In the summer this can be an idyllic place, far different from the winter, when gales lash the coastline. Casual visitors to this piece of wasteland would be amazed to learn of the large mill community that once lived and worked here.

The miller standing outside Fletching Mill.

ABOVE: The unusual flat roof extension at Fletching Mill in October 1938. (AS) BELOW: The newly renovated Boringwheel Mill in 1897. (AT)

ABOVE: Boringwheel Mill looks rather dilapidated in 1975. LEFT: Shortbridge Mill as a store in 1954 (SPAB), and RIGHT: its unusual pentrough arrangement in 1991.

43

ABOVE: The idyllic Plumpton Place Mill and pond, LEFT: the small
Plumpton Upper Mill and waterwheel and RIGHT: the waterwheel
and tail race at Plumpton Mill – in 1996.

ABOVE: Plumpton Mill in 1996. BELOW: Discarded edge runner millstones at the site of Barcombe Oil Mill.

ABOVE: Barcombe Oil Mill at the turn of the century. (VE)
BELOW: Barcombe Mill on fire in March 1939.

ABOVE: The downstream view of Barcombe Mill with its massive boiler chimney. BELOW: The aftermath of the fire. (AS)

ABOVE: The remnants of Barcombe Mill in 1939. BELOW: The rail head to Bishopstone Tide Mills in 1883.

ABOVE: The view through the village at Bishopstone Tide Mills, and
BELOW: The Mills, both in 1883. (BRL)

49

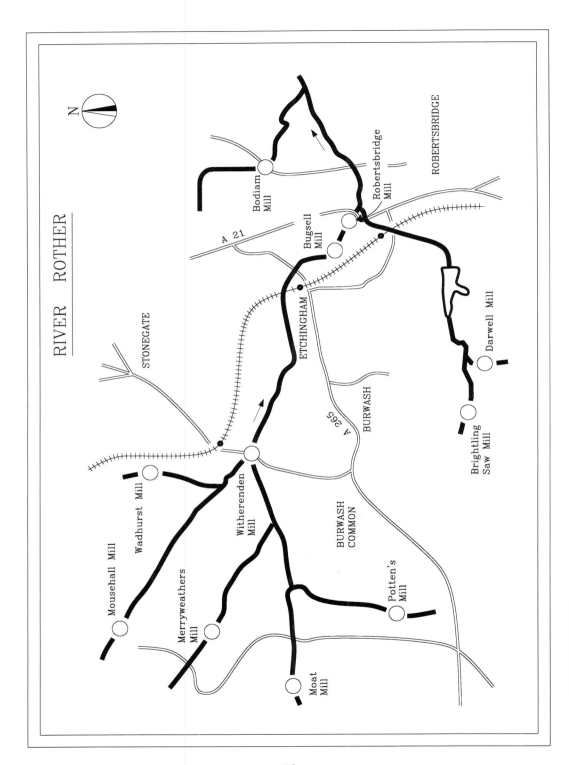

RIVER ROTHER

N

STONEGATE

A 21

Bodiam
Mill

Bugsell
Mill

ROBERTSBRIDGE

Robertsbridge
Mill

ETCHINGHAM

Darwell Mill

BURWASH

A 265

Brightling
Saw Mill

Mousehall Mill

Wadhurst Mill

Witherenden
Mill

Merryweathers
Mill

BURWASH
COMMON

Potten's
Mill

Moat
Mill

RIVER ROTHER

POTTEN'S MILL *Broad Oak*
Tributary to River Rother TQ 613 242 — At end of private track one mile northeast of Broad Oak.

Potten's Mill has gone, but its name is perpetuated by the former mill house, now renamed Potten's Mill Farm.

The mill is described in a settlement of 1623 as a messuage, barns, buildings and a watermill belonging to John Crouch. He made his will in 1655 and left the property to his son-in-law Thomas Parson, who eventually ran the mill until at least 1687, and upon his death his son Thomas carried on. The mill continued in the ownership of the same family until 1788, when the estate was sold for £1,108 to the owner of the nearby Heathfield Park. The mill continued to be known as Parson's Mill for some time after and appeared on the 1813 Ordnance Survey 1in map as such. Curiously, the rate books for 1807 and as late as 1842 refer to it as the 'late Potten's Mill'. James Relf was the miller until 1858. Relf had been preceded at this mill by Arthur Knight and William Skinner in 1827 and 1830 respectively.

Little more is known about the mill, although it has a wooden waterwheel and was marked as 'Corn' on the 1874 Ordnance Survey 25in map. The map also shows that the mill was long and thin and set into the pond embankment. It is presumed that it closed down towards the end of the 19th century.

The large millpond is still in water, but following extensive regrading of the pond embankment all traces of the mill have disappeared.

MOAT MILL *Mayfield*
Tributary to River Rother TQ 591 249 — At end of private track southwest of Mayfield.

Ernest Straker, writing in his book *Wealden Iron*, states that this site was probably used in connection with that industry due to the existence of cinder slag found here.

Moat Mill is the highest mill on the River Rother and is certainly not an ancient mill site. The earliest record of this mill is found on Gream's map of 1795, while shortly after, in 1803, Samuel Thompson, the miller, could contribute three sacks of flour during threat of invasion, according to the Defence Schedules. The mill had stopped working by the turn of the century and the buildings were marked as 'Moat Mill Farm' on the 1911 Ordnance Survey 6in map.

Kelly's directory makes reference to Benjamin Thomsett and William Bonwick as occupiers at separate times in the middle of the 19th century but, overall, little else is known about its history.

When the mill was incorporated as part of the mill house and converted into residential accommodation, the majority of the wooden machinery was fortunately left in place. The 2ft diameter solid wooden wallower, a rare example, is of special interest, along with the wooden pit wheel and crown wheel. The crown wheel has two wooden shafts off it, one which drove a wire machine (now removed) and the other that originally worked a sack hoist and a smutter. It is uncommon to find no cast iron machinery inside the mill, as it was common practice to replace wooden drive machinery during the middle to late 19th century.

Adjacent to the flank wall of the mill are the remains of a small iron overshot waterwheel, manufactured by Neves of Heathfield, 9ft in diameter by 4ft wide, but due to a lack of live water it now lies partially submerged in a pool of stagnant water. Although the framework and a few buckets remain, it is sad to see this once proud waterwheel in its existing predicament.

The mill is built of brick to the first floor with tarred weatherboarding above, under a tiled roof. Externally, the dormer windows in the roof and other modern alterations have rather spoilt the appearance of the mill. The ponding arrangements are unusual as, almost as an afterthought, the river was widened nearly to the mill dam, according to the 1874 Ordnance Survey 25in map.

Moat Mill was only a small building, with 2-pairs of stones, but the wooden machinery is exceptional and should be retained in the mill.

MERRYWEATHERS MILL *Mayfield*

Tributary to River Rother TQ 608 272 — At end of private track one mile east of Mayfield.

This mill is hidden away at the end of a long driveway to 'Merryweathers', the house from which it takes its name.

A mill on this site is probably that referred to in the will of John Moore in March 1560. This mentions the implements and other moveable objects at 'Marywethers Mill'. Later, in 1650, reference is made to William Weston holding a messuage and a watermill here. In March 1931 a notice in the *Sussex Advertiser* was addressed to people who may have outstanding claims, or demands, on the estate of John Weston, late of Merryweathers Mill. From this it would appear that the Weston family had been associated with this mill for many years. Further on in the year the mill was advertised for sale, by auction, together with nearby Merryweathers Windmill. The Tithe Map Apportionment of 1843 refers to William Packham as the occupier, with interests in both the wind and watermill, while a trade directory entry in 1899 gives Hannah Brain as the miller. After this all references to the mill cease and it seems to have closed down at a time when many others were doing likewise on economic grounds.

Some time after the closure the building was converted into a house and the machinery sold for scrap. The mill is an attractive brick and weatherboarded building kept in a good state of repair, while at the rear the former millpond has now become a feature of the landscaped garden.

MOUSEHALL MILL *Tidebrook*

Tributary to River Rother TQ 609 297 — Adjacent to an unmade road in Tidebrook.

The mill still survives, although for some time it has been incorporated into residential accommodation and forms part of the mill house. It is not known when the existing mill was established here, but it would appear to date from the beginning of the 18th century, while the mill house is of 16th-century origin, with three bays. In 1709 John Filtness is recorded as inheriting the mill from his father, he in turn being succeeded by his son later in the century. The Standen family took over the tenancy in 1772 and remained in occupation until 1871, after which John Standen left the mill.

The mill is marked on the 1910 Ordnance Survey map, but by then it was disused, the mill and house having been purchased in 1897 by a Mr Haynes, who had no interest in running the mill. The mill stood derelict until about 1938, when it was converted into a weekend residence. The watercourse through the site was diverted and the gardens landscaped, thus removing all traces of the tail race. The millpond has dried up, but its outline is still discernable. The wheelpit survives and the bricked-up aperture, which accommodated the overshot waterwheel axle shaft, can be clearly seen, but apart from this nothing else remains to indicate its former use. Propped up against the wall of the mill house is a very old millstone, which carries the inscription 'FF + GC 1687' which, if authentic, could refer to a member of the Filtness family who were in residence at the time.

The mill is constructed in brick, timber and sandstone blocks and now forms part of a very desirable residence, with little visible association with its past.

WADHURST MILL *Wadhurst*
Tributary to River Rother TQ 640 286 — By a small road southeast of Wadhurst Park.

This is nothing to be seen of Wadhurst Mill and the site has disappeared into obscurity. A mill was used here in connection with the iron industry, but when it was replaced by a corn mill is unknown. Although there is a well-constructed pond overflow 200 yards upstream from the road bridge, recent landscaping work has removed any traces that may have existed to indicate the site of the mill.

The owner of a nearby house has dug up several cannon balls over recent years, confirming its past association with the iron industry.

WITHERENDEN MILL *Ticehurst*
River Rother TQ 654 269 — To the southwest of Stonegate railway station.

There does not appear to be any evidence available to suggest that this is an ancient mill site. Witherenden Mill was situated beside the River Rother, in a small valley to the north of Witherenden Hill, but no traces exist of the last mill to have stood here.

From 1743 to 1818 the mill was in the occupation of Joseph Newington and later, in 1820, the family erected a windmill at the top of Witherenden Hill and used it in conjunction with their watermill. The two mills worked together, until the windmill was blown down during a gale in January 1882. The Newingtons were still in operation here in 1840, according to the Tithe Map Apportionment, but during the 1850s Charles Martin came from Dunster's Mill to work the mill in a partnership with Brissenden. This association continued until about 1867, when both millers retired from the business. The mill was advertised for sale, along with the windmill, in October 1867, with George Steadman taking up the lease on the watermill shortly afterwards — but he only stayed for a few years. The last occupier was Henry Wickham, he taking over from Walter Hicks. He ran the mill until closure in 1927. It was during Wickham's tenancy that the mill caught fire, on 13 December 1899, and was totally destroyed, according to a report in *The Miller*. The damage was estimated at £1,600, which included the machinery, and the trade magazine described it as 'a total loss'.

A postcard view of the mill burnt down in 1899 reveals it to be constructed in a jumble of building styles, as there were four separate buildings all joined together. Three of them were built of brick and timber, with odd pieces of tarred weatherboarding and half-hipped roofs of different sizes, while the other remaining building was built entirely of wood. The new replacement mill, in complete contrast, was built to four floors in brick under a slate roof — a totally functional building.

When Sidney Ashdown visited the site in April 1939 he reported that the mill was reduced to nothing, but according to a report nine years later the ground floor remained, together with the internal waterwheel and odd pieces of machinery. The waterwheel survived until the 1960s, driving a saw bench, but only the outline of the tumbling bay survives to mark the site.

BUGSELL MILL.   F.VV.G

BUGSELL MILL *Hurst Green*
River Rother TQ 724 256 — At end of track south of Haremere Hill.

This is another mill site that was first used for the iron industry, for it was recorded that a forge was at work here in 1588. Ernest Straker, in his book *Wealden Iron*, writes that by 1644 the forge was in ruins and that a corn mill was erected here in 1777.

The mill was identified as 'Bugshill Mill' on the 1813 Ordnance Survey 1in map, but became Bugsell Mill afterwards. As the mill was located in an isolated position it could be assumed that this was a small mill, but it did have one unusual feature. This tall but thin watermill had two wooden waterwheels, one overshot and one breastshot (probably a flood wheel), positioned at each end of the mill. Although each wheel worked 2-pairs of stones, an unusual gearing arrangement between the two respective crown wheels enabled either set of stones to be worked by each waterwheel.

According to the Tithe Map Apportionment of 1843, Thomas Noakes was the occupier, he being followed by Samuel Burgess, with William Russell the last miller when the mill closed down in about 1924.

Bugsell Mill comprised three floors in brick and timber on stone foundations, and prior to its demolition in 1953 the breastshot waterwheel was still used occasionally for oat crushing. A visit to the site in 1991 revealed only the remains of some wooden shafting, along with some odd brickwork, with two french burr millstones lying beside the mill house.

ROBERTSBRIDGE MILL *Robertsbridge*
River Rother TQ 737 241 — Adjacent to Northbridge Street north of Robertsbridge.

According to the book *The History of Salehurst*, written in 1914, mills have stood on this site for at least six centuries, under the name of Ockham Mill (probably in the control of Robertsbridge Abbey in its early days).

There was a large iron furnace in Robertsbridge, according to a sale advertisement that appeared in the *Sussex Weekly Advertiser* on 7 January 1788, which indicated that the buildings could be converted into a large corn mill. It is likely that this furnace was on, or very near, the existing site and was probably converted into a flour mill, with William Hilder the miller. According to *Kelly's* trade directories, it remained in the occupation of the Hilder family until 1874, although the old furnace buildings had long been replaced. A photograph of the mill taken in 1865 shows it to be of brick and white weatherboarding, constructed in the style typical of south-east England. This was a large mill and contained 5-pairs of stones, with the power derived from two external waterwheels, one a breast and the other overshot. A steam engine was later installed to supplement the water supply during the summer months. This mill was pulled down in 1878 and replaced by a five-storey brick-built mill with machinery supplied by John Smith of the Grove Iron Works, Carshalton, Surrey. An article in *The Miller* of 7 May 1894 described the replacement machinery fitted in that year:

'Robertsbridge Mill, Mr James Hodson. John Smith system. Previous to being rebuilt in 1878, the then existing building was some hundreds of years old. Mr James Hodson, whose family had been engaged in farming for generations, took over the old mill, now called the Robertsbridge Steam and Roller Mills, in the year 1876 and two years after had erected the present substantial building.

The mill at first contained 7-pairs of millstones, but a few years later, in order to cope with competition, Mr Hodson added some Jonathan Discs to the plant. Additional improvements were added as time went by, but at last Mr Hodson decided to have a roller mill in order to keep abreast of the times, and gave the order to erect the plant to John Smith, the well-known milling engineer and millwright of Carshalton, Surrey. The plant is 5-sack. A portion of the ground floor is occupied by the wheel-house, which houses an overshot waterwheel 11ft wide by 9ft diameter. On the north side of the wheel is a 33in 'Little Giant' turbine.'

The turbine had been installed in 1883, according to an article in *The Miller*, and was reported as running with entire satisfaction right through the heavy floods of that year. Disaster struck the mill on the morning of 5 December 1902 when a fire broke out, resulting in the entire mill being burnt to the ground (even though Mr Hodson was the Captain of the local fire brigade and the fire engine was kept on site). The nearby mill house suffered damage but the large brick-built grain store, attached at right-angles to the mill, escaped serious harm.

Undaunted by this setback, Mr Hodson set about constructing a new mill on the site, similar in design to his previous mill, but four storeys high. Simons of Manchester installed a 3½ sack roller mill to supplement the millstones, powered by the waterwheel and turbine, which survived the fire. This turbine was eventually replaced in the mid-1920s by a new Armfield Two Gate 'River' Turbine, although it was subsequently not found to be as efficient as hoped for, and could only power 2-pairs of stones. The waterwheel was retained to power the remaining pair of stones. In 1929, the beam engine, supplied by Simons, was removed, together with the engine house and a 50ft-high chimney at the back of the mill.

The ailing flour mill was saved when electricity came to Robertsbridge in 1931 and Thomas Dadswell, who had taken over the mill some 10 years ealier, installed a 40hp generator. However, almost immediately afterwards he sold his flour quota to the Millers Mutual Association. In 1941 the Ministry of Food instructed Dadswell to start milling again and he contacted a milling engineer, Alfred Tattersall, who supplied a two break two reduction mill, made in one unit, being the largest available. It was conveyed to the mill by railway, with a hole being made in the mill to gain entry, while other milling equipment came from Uckfield Mill. The mill started in June 1942 and was worked day and night to comply with the Ministry's request of 100 tons of flour per month, most of which went to Hobb's Army Barracks at East Grinstead.

The mill continued working after the war, but by the end of the 1940s stone-ground flour went out of fashion. Thomas Dadswell's son, also named Thomas, continued at the mill until he sold it in 1966. Despite being in the ownership of the Dadswell family from 1931 untl 1966, the mill traded under the name of James Hodson Ltd, thus perpetuating the business name from the 19th century. In 1966 the mill complex was purchased by Rank Animal Feed and later by SCATS Ltd, who erected a number of large warehouses here. SCATS still occupy the site (1991) for the production and storage of animal foodstuffs, but using machinery far removed from what previously operated here. The old flour mill, built in 1903, still remains and is used for storage while, from the outside, the frame of the waterwheel and the turbine can be seen beneath the mill. As the pit floor has been concreted over, there is now no access to inspect this machinery, except by boat!

One of the most interesting features associated with this mill was the method used to supply a head of water to the site. An artificial channel was cut from the River Rother about a mile and a half upstream, following the natural contours of the land to provide a fall. This channel was cut several centuries ago and is an astute piece of water engineering, so designed to parallel the existing course of the river but to be 16ft to 20ft above, thereby providing the necessary head of water at the mill.

It cannot be said that the proprietors of this mill were loathe to change and introduce ways of making the mill business more efficient. In 1951 the mill possessed four large

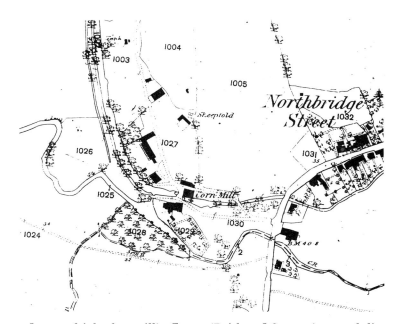

Bedford vans from which the mill's flour, 'Pride of Sussex', was delivered all over Sussex and Kent. Also, following the closure of the freight traffic on the Robertsbridge to Tenterden railway in 1961, Thomas Dadswell purchased a railway engine to continue importing grain using the short railway spur line originally built to the mill in August 1903. This was obviously a shrewd financial investment, as the majority of the grain was delivered in 20-ton bulk wagons direct from Avonmouth Docks. One of the last deliveries took place in May 1964, when the locomotive puffed along the weed-infested track towards the mill with just a single wagon. After ending its service at the mill, the 0-6-0 tank engine was acquired by the Kent & East Sussex Railway and restored back to use in the 1980s. This also meant the end of the coal merchants' business operated from the mill (400 to 500 wagonloads of coal were delivered by rail per annum). Robertsbridge Mill was constantly modernised to keep it a viable business concern, but it finally succumbed to the rivalry of modern milling techniques. The mill buildings still survive (1991). Though disused, nothing can deny the fact that this was one of the largest and busiest watermills in East Sussex.

BODIAM MILL *Bodiam*
Kent Ditch — tributary to River Rother TQ 782 267 — West side of road north of Bodiam.

Bodiam is quite rightly known for its classic moated castle, which was established here in the late 14th century. The village is small and the former watermill, situated next to the road to Sandcross Cross, has all but been forgotten since it was destroyed by fire in the late 1940s. The mill used the power of the Kent Ditch which, at this point, forms the county boundary, with the mill in Sussex and the waterwheel in Kent.

In the 1803 Defence Schedules this mill is described as small and unable to grind sufficient flour for the inhabitants. However, it must have been rebuilt, for according to a sale notice in the *Sussex Advertiser* in May 1584 the mill is described as substantial.

This does not appear to be the site of a Domesday Mill as a reference in 1385 refers to a plan to divert a watercourse to the mill in 'Bodyham' and this is probably still the small leat that fed the mill in its latter working days. While the Kent Ditch was in no way navigable, Bodiam Mill no doubt took advantage of its close proximity to the Eastern Rother Navigation, which passed just to the south of the village, for the transfer of wheat and flour.

A fire insurance policy relates that in February 1792, William Longley, miller, insured the contents of his thatched mill. Certainly the thatched mill did not survive the years and it was probably demolished to make way for the mill referred to earlier.

From at least 1854 until 1909, the mill was operated by the Collins family, with Edward following Thomas in 1866. The sale of the mill took place in 1854, when it was described as a 'good water corn and substantial mill, driving 4-pairs of stone, long established and in good trade, with residence situated upon the stream dividing the parishes and counties'. Included in the sale was a windmill at Sandhurst, which had five sails. Charles Bannister was the miller from 1911, but after this date all trade references cease.

When the mill was destroyed by fire, the adjoining mill house survived, along with the waterwheel. However, the years have taken their toll on this exposed waterwheel and its top half has collapsed, giving it a rather flat appearance. The short leat from the Kent Ditch no longer exists, or the narrow millpond that was behind the mill.

BRIGHTLING SAW MILL *Brightling*
Tributary to River Rother TQ 686 201 — 400 yards west side of road south of Brightling.

In 1968 this saw mill was complete and probably still capable of work, by tractor power, but recent events have now reduced this saw mill to a ruin, and the work benches will surely rot away. That the mill survived with its machinery for so long is quite remarkable, but the sad fact is that the mill's demise was caused by a combination of general neglect and storm damage in October 1987, when a tree fell across the building. An application to demolish this Grade II listed buiding was refused, and the roof was then removed and lay in a heap on the earth floor.

Fortunately, the framework of the cast iron overshot waterwheel remains, 16ft in diameter by 3ft wide and mounted on a 6in square axle shaft, with an inscription on its rim revealing that it was manufactured by 'Neve Bros' in 1891. It could be assumed that this date indicated the founding of the saw mill, but a building is marked as such on the 1873-4 Ordnance Survey 6in map, although a small farmer's-own-use type watermill has preceded it. This original saw mill was a most unusually-shaped building entirely constructed in wood, and a photograph shows the waterwheel installed in 1891.

In 1877, the estate was advertised for sale in the *Sussex Advertiser*:

'To be sold by auction on 11 July. Included in the estate . . . valuable adjuncts to the property are the water saw mill, used for converting the timber required for repairs, and the brickyard, both for home use and for sale in the neighbourhood.'

The present saw mill was built at the turn of the century and the date '1902' cut on the brickwork inside, would suggest a likely date. The brick and timber building is situated below a high pond embankment, and the water was controlled onto the wheel *via* a tall wooden starter box.

This is a sad site in terms of industrial history. Nearby stands a derelict house, while at the back of the mill lies the body shell of an old cart, half buried in the ground. The millpond survives as ever, but this cannot hide the fact that a valuable and working example of a water powered saw mill has fallen into total disrepair.

DARWELL MILL *Brightling*
Darwell Stream — tributary to River Rother TQ 696 199 — Adjacent to forestry track southeast of Brightling.

There was a large iron furnace at Darwell Wood in 1649 and this survived until 1763 (it was dismantled in 1787 and the site lies completely submerged beneath Darwell reservoir). Just upstream from this site was Darwell Mill, probably erected here some time after the cessation of the iron furnace — although no mill is marked on the 1813 Ordnance Survey 1in map. It was certainly in existence before July 1827, as the *Sussex Weekly Advertiser* announced the sale of the mill:
'To be sold by order of the Devisees in Trust for sale under the wills of Mr Edward Hilder and Mr John Hillman. Darvell Mill at Brightling, let to Rose Fuller at £7-0-0 . . .'
A note was added to this article to the effect that the property was for sale along with Dudwell Watermill and Burwash Windmill.

The mill at various times was known as Darvell Mill, but from the 1859 Tithe Map Apportionment onwards, it was always referred to as Darwell Mill. William Clark was the miller here, with Charles and Frederick Clark the occupiers in 1878. All trade directories cease after this date and it is presumed that the mill closed down. It was marked disused on the 1931 Ordnance Survey 6in map but was gone by the early 1950s.

For a watermill building that survived until quite late, the identification of the site is almost impossible as it lies buried in dense undergrowth. The cast iron overshot waterwheel survived until the 1930s, but all that now remains is a 5ft high brick wall that once formed part of the millpond embankment, the remains of a wooden pentrough, discarded masonry and a tumbling bay.

The site now forms part of Darwell Wood, which is managed by the Forestry Commission, but it is once again disappointing to find so little remains.

OTHER MILLS ON THE RIVER ROTHER

MAYFIELD OLD MILL
TQ 586 245

This is a site whose past is shrouded in mystery. It would have been a corn mill originally but it was converted for electricity and then pumping. There are remains near to Old Mill Farm.

LEFT: Moat Mill in a semi derelict condition in 1902, BELOW: the partly submerged waterwheel in 1991 and RIGHT: the rare wooden wallower.

60

ABOVE: Four different building styles compete at Witherenden Mill in 1898; LEFT: the new mill built following the fire in 1901 (both VE). RIGHT: Mousehall Mill as a house conversion in 1991.

ABOVE: The brick and timber Robertsbridge Mill in 1860, with LEFT:
delivery wagons outside about 1888; RIGHT: the work force towards
the end of the 19th century. (both TD)

ABOVE: The separate channels for waterwheel and turbine at
Robertsbridge Mill in 1902, (TD) and BELOW: a steam delivery
wagon outside. (TD)

ABOVE: A 'P' Class railway engine owned and used by Robertsbridge Mill to deliver grain, and BELOW: a fleet of delivery lorries outside in 1951. (both TD)

LEFT: The only remaining feature of Bodiam Mill in April 1939. (AS)
RIGHT: The framework of the overshot waterwheel at Brightling Saw
Mill in 1991. BELOW: The old Brightling Saw Mill just before the turn
of the century, (FG) and INSET: the replacement Brightling Saw Mill
built in 1902 and photographed in 1968. (SPAB)

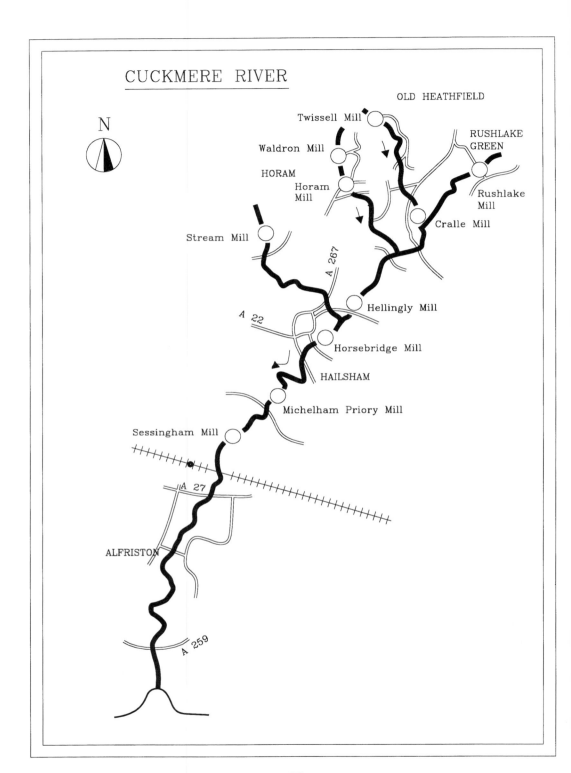

CUCKMERE RIVER

OLD HEATHFIELD

Twissell Mill

N

RUSHLAKE
GREEN

Waldron Mill

HORAM

Horam
Mill

Rushlake
Mill

Cralle Mill

Stream Mill

A 267

Hellingly Mill

A 22

Horsebridge Mill

HAILSHAM

Michelham Priory Mill

Sessingham Mill

A 27

ALFRISTON

A 259

RIVER CUCKMERE

RUSHLAKE MILL *Warbleton*
Tributary to River Cuckmere TQ 622 180 — At the end of a private track one mile east of Warbleton.

Rushlake Mill, formerly known as Charne Mill, was an ancient mill site reputedly dating back to 1200. The first unequivocal reference was in 1542 and thereafter a mill on this site was regularly mentioned in deeds and manorial records. It is not until the beginning of the 19th century that details emerge about the last mill on this site and the occupiers. By 1882 at least, a windmill called 'Smith's Mill' was working in conjunction with the watermill and in August of that year James Eastern was charged with breaking and entering into both mills, which were being worked by Henry Blackburn. Blackburn was still here in 1848, according to the Tithe Apportionment, but seven years later John Baitup was the recorded miller and the mill stayed in the same family until 1918. In 1909 a small Clayton and Butterworth engine was installed and directly geared to the crown wheel, to supplement the ailing water supply.

After closure, the mill stood derelict until 1933, at which time it was demolished after a fire. A report in May 1935 stated that the overshot waterwheel (15ft in diameter) had been removed in 1934.

According to the 1874 Ordnance Survey 25in map this was only a small mill and, unusually, the water bypass was taken off the main river before the pond, but the site of the mill can easily be identified to the northeast of the mill house. A brick-lined pentrough marks the position of the waterwheel set below the dried-up millpond.

TWISSELL'S MILL *Old Heathfield*
Tributary to River Cuckmere TQ 594 197 — By a private track southwest of Old Heathfield.

There is some evidence to suggest hat the site of Twissell's Mill was first established in the 13th century when all the land at Twissle, Thorn and Farnstrete was given to Otham Priory (which later moved to Bayham). A witness to this transaction was William de Warbleton, who was in possession of a watermill at the time.

The next reference appeared in 1633, when Christopher Warnet held a messuage and a watermill called Twissell Mill. Over the next hundred years, there were a number of references to the mill in various ownership and tenancy transactions.

The mill site lies to the southwest of Old Heathfield and, along with Cross in Hand Windmill, it provided flour to the developing village of Heathfield. From the beginning of the 19th century the mill was in the ownership of Thomas and then John Balcombe, to at least 1844. They were followed by Samuel and William Noakes before the mill was taken over by John Fuller in 1849, he being the last miller here. It is marked as a corn mill on the 1874 Ordnance Survey 25in map but later on all trade references to the mill cease. The mill remained in a rather dilapidated condition, but complete until destroyed by fire in the early 1930s. From a contemporary photograph dating from the early 1900s, the mill appeared to be an extremely old building set below, but not part of, the embankment of the millpond.

The present owner of the mill site has obtained planning permission to erect a waterpowered textile mill here and a sale notice in the *Sussex Courier* of 5 July 1996 advertises the site for sale, but there would not appear to be enough water and it seems unlikely to be built. The site is not easy to find and only some scattered brickwork is to be seen.

CRALLE MILL *Warbleton*
Tributary to River Cuckmere TQ 610 160 — In meadows below Cralle Place a mile and a half south of Warbleton.

There appear to be variations of the spelling of this former watermill site, located to the south of Warbleton. Ernest Straker, in his book *Wealden Iron*, refers to the furnace and forge on this site, at 'Cralle' (which survived until recorded as 'ruined' in 1664). The 1874 Ordnance Survey 25in map marks the site as 'Crawle Mill' but gives no definition of its use. Following the demise of the iron industry at this site a watermill was erected and in February 1820 the *Sussex Weekly Advertiser* reported on the sale of 'Crawl Mill' owing to the death of John Saunders, who had previously been in control of Waldron Mill. It would appear that the mill remained unsold, for all references to the site cease after the date of the sale, though the mill building remained in existence until 1908.

There are still vague traces of the pond bay to be seen, but in the 170 years since the mill ceased working nature has taken over and returned the area to meadowland. The mill was well away from the local villages in the area and the Ordnance Survey map shows it to have been be a small mill, probably only containing 2-pairs of stones.

On the higher ground above the mill site is Cralle Place, a 16th-century house of great age and distinction.

WALDRON MILL *Waldron*
Tributary to River Cuckmere TQ 568 186 — North of an unclassified road from Sharp's Corner to Little London.

The existing group of buildings on this site is known as 'Leopard's Mill', a name of no relevant historical background. This was formerly referred to as Waldron Mill, and the old mill now forms the centre section of the group of buildings set below a high pond embankment.

The area around the buildings has been extensively landscaped and it is difficult to make out the course of the original waterways, although the overflow channel and tumbling bay have been left untouched.

This is little known information about the mill, although an article in the *Sussex Weekly Advertiser* of 30 January 1797 announced the sale of Waldron Windmill. Prospective applicants were told to contact John Saunders at Waldron Watermill. Saunders also had control of the nearby Cralle Mill.

The last trade directory entry for the windmill was in 1874, after which it apparently closed down, and only a worn millstone by the front door of the mill house indicates the former use of the site.

HORAM MILL *Horam*
Waldron Gill — tributary to River Cuckmere TQ 583 173 — At the end of a track south of Vines Cross Road.

There appears to be no evidence to suggest that this is an early mill site, while the last mill was very small and without doubt was the mill shown on Budgeon's map of 1725. The mill was located down a small track that leads to a small farm and nurseries, but it did only an average trade in flour. This is surprising, as Horam was a small but thriving village and there was little competition from other watermills or windmills in the area.

The Land Tax Returns and Rate Books for the area reveal some facts about this mill. From 1780 to 1830 the owner of the mill was John Fuller. Curiously, the mill is referred to at this time as 'Stream Mill' but it should not be confused with the other mill of the same name, the building of which still exists, at Chiddingly, some 2½ miles to the southwest. According to the *Sussex Advertiser* of September 1881, the mill was to be sold at auction, and it was purchased by Henry Sutton, who became the last miller. The mill had only 2-pairs of stones, which were driven by a layshaft. After commercial milling ceased in the 1930s, the mill did not remain idle over the ensuing years for, in 1939, the waterwheel was used to drive a saw bench. However, the following year the waterwheel was removed for scrap, no doubt to help the war effort, and the empty mill was used as a store for pig food, until it burnt down.

It was a brick and white weatherboarded timber mill with an iron waterwheel, and the front door was at the top of six roughly cut steps in the pond embankment. The brick arched tunnel that channelled the water from the pond onto the wheel has survived, but nothing else remains to indicate the use of the site.

HELLINGLY MILL *Hellingly*
River Cuckmere TQ 585 125 — Northwest of village, on the north side of road.

Hellingly Mill is an attractive brick and timber framed building of three floors, presently under full restoration, and stands on an ancient mill site dating back to at least 1256, when it was in the ownership of the Abbot of Battle.

The present mill dates back to 1749, a time when the mill house was also rebuilt from a single-storey dwelling. Old stone blocks in the base wall of the mill are evidence of an earlier undershot wheel-driven mill.

The 1749 rebuild had an oak vertical shaft and wooden cog wheels, all of which were replaced in 1860 by cast iron equivalents supplied by Upfield of Catsfield. The cast iron spur wheel was a single casting of smaller diameter so that it could fit through the door of the mill.

At the turn of the 19th century the mill was under the control of Stephen Kennard, who came from a well-known and respected Sussex milling family and, according to the Defence Schedules of 1803, could supply eight sacks of flour daily using his own wheat. The 1840 Tithe Apportionment refers to it as Stonehouse Mill, obviously after the nearby farm just to the west of the mill. Benjamin Heaver had taken over by 1855 and it remained in Heaver family ownership until just before the turn of the century, when the following sale notice appeared in *The Miller* of 10 May 1897:

'To be sold by auction at the White Hart Hotel, Lewes, on the 25 May, by order of the Trustees of the will of Benjamin Heaver. The Water Corn Mill known as Hellingly Mill, Sussex, with overshot wheel driving three pairs of stones, granary, coach house, bakehouse (with 4-bushel oven) and a dwelling house.'

It obviously remained unsold, for it was advertised for sale in August 1901 at the Crown Hotel at Hailsham. According to *Kelly's* directory of 1907, the Howard brothers were at the mill and they stayed there until 1915, following which Percy Morris was in control. When the last commercial trade directory entry appeared in 1922, Morris was the occupier.

Although the mill utilised the power of the Cuckmere River, extensive bore holes by the Eastbourne Water Works Co, reduced the water levels to such an extent that a portable steam engine was used until the closure of the mill in 1922. By 1924 the mill stood derelict, and remained as such until 1938, when new owners turned it into the 'Old Water Mill Tea Room' and fortunately left most of the remaining machinery and hursting intact. After the war it was bought by the playwright John Osborne, who converted the middle floor of the mill into a study, and it was here that he wrote perhaps his most famous play, *Look Back in Anger*. Osborne advertised the mill for sale in 1971 and included seven acres of land, together with its trout water (although it is difficult to imagine this particular breed of fish being found in the Cuckmere River today).

In 1974 the property was bought by Jonathan Minns, founder and director of the British Engineerium at Hove, and he immediately set about the restoration of the mill, which had been kept in reasonable condition by the previous occupier. The first task was to replace the old waterwheel bearings, and in 1984 a new iron overshot waterwheel was fitted. The design of the wheel was carried out 'in house' and was manufactured by the now defunct St Pancras Ironworks at Chichester. The waterwheel was made to the exact dimensions of its predecessor, 7ft 6in wide by 10ft wide, and it looks a fine sight when viewed from the old road bridge in front of the mill. A new penstock, sluice gates and oak hursting also had to be manufactured and, along with other work, the restoration of the mill is nearing completion.

Before the involvement of the water company, the Cuckmere River was widened just upstream from the mill to create a millpond, with the overflow taken off by way of a sluice, thus creating a lower pond on the east side of the mill house. Originally, both sides of the mill had white-painted weatherboarding, but this was removed on the east side when the tea rooms were in operation and it remains thus today.

Without doubt, the restoration carried out on Hellingly Mill has certainly preserved the mill building, and the fact that is machinery is also being saved and replaced where necessary ensures the future of this typical rural Sussex Mill.

STREAM MILL *Chiddingly*

Bull River — tributary to River Cuckmere TQ 556 155 — At the end of a private track one mile northeast of Chiddingly.

During the 16th and 17th centuries this was an important site used extensively in connection with the iron industry. The site began as a forge and later, in 1597, a furnace was constructed and, in 1692, guns were cast here. The furnace was marked on Budgeon's map of 1724, but not on any further documents.

The construction of a corn mill commonly followed the cessation of iron casting. Furnaces and forges required a considerable amount of water, which was also an attractive feature for a prospective mill owner, and this was certainly the case at this site. The pond was once very expansive but it is now nothing more than a swamp, with little evidence of standing water, and it is suggested that the corn mill was erected on the former iron site, which, if correct, obliterated any remains of that industry. The old corn mill has been converted into living accommodation and, outwardly, bears no resemblance to a watermill. The mill site is isolated and well away from a public road. The mill stopped working in the 1930s and, according to an inspection in 1941, it contained 2-pairs of stones driven by a layshaft. The machinery had been removed in 1938, after which it became a store for chicken food. At that time the roof was replaced by red-painted galvanised sheeting.

It is not known when the mill was established here but in 1803 John Lashmar was the recorded occupier of the mill, according to an entry in the Defence Schedules, and it appears that when the mill closed down, William Gorringe was the miller.

Stream Mill has outwardly lost its connection with the past and the house and garden bear little evidence of its previous use, but this is a peaceful and tranquil location.

HORSEBRIDGE MILL *Upper Horsebridge*
River Cuckmere TQ 582 113 — North of Upper Horsebridge Road, Upper Horsebridge.

Horsebridge Mill is an imposing building that took its supply of water power from the Cuckmere River, which passes under the mill (a leat being taken off to power the waterwheel). The mill building is now devoid of any milling machinery and is used as an engineering factory.

The present building was rebuilt in 1884, following a disastrous fire, as reported in the *Sussex Advertiser* of 30 September 1884:

'To be sold by auction on 21 October, 1884, the site of Horsebridge Water and Steam Corn Mill. The property comprises the aforesaid remains of the well constructed mill lately burnt out, including the walls and the loose fallen bricks, the large waterwheel, nearly intact, shaft and large cog wheels in mill, the 10hp horizontal engine with double cylinder (by Clayton & Shuttleworth) just out of repair, a new 20hp boiler (by W. H. Nicholson and Son of Newark on Trent) undamaged, the boiler house and shaft in nearly perfect state. Also dwelling house and land. The mill has recently been destroyed by fire and the owners and occupiers being men advanced in years, are not practical millers, are desirous to leave the reconstruction to younger hands, and an opportunity is thus given to an energetic man to fit up a new building with modern machinery under his own superintendence.'

This does not appear to be an ancient mill site, being first shown on Budgeon's map of 1724, although a John Mepham was recorded as the miller in the sale particulars of Hellingly Place.

The former mill was built at the end of the 18th century, for in 1792 Henry Earl, the proprietor, advertised the mill for sale and stated that it was newly built and contained 4-pairs of stones. Later, in 1829, the mill was quoted as containing 3-pairs of stones and being capable of grinding 10 to 15 loads of wheat per week under the supervision of Samuel Ballard, the miller. John Hilder was the next proprietor, in 1832, and, according to an advertisement that appeared in the *Sussex Advertiser*, the mill was 'now in good repair'.

71

Horsebridge Mill was never a 'family-owned' type of mill as there was a succession of occupiers here, especially so during the 19th century. George Goldsmith was the recorded occupier according to the Tithe Apportionment published in 1843, and he appeared to continue at this mill until 1851, when Michael Martin took over. He in turn was replaced by George Kenward Jnr, who advertised in the *Sussex Advertiser* for a miller here in July 1871. Kenward was responsible for installing steam power to the mill, for in the sale particulars that appeared in the *Sussex Advertiser* of 20 July 1880 the mill was described as follows:

'Sale of Horsebridge Water and Steam Mills at the Star, Lewes, on July 13 comprising a moderate and well constructed mill of four floors and driving 4-pairs of wheat and 1-pair of peak stones. The mill is driven by the Cuckmere River and is also fitted with a 10hp horizontal double cylinder steam engine. The whole lot is freehold and there is a mortgage on it of £2,200.' It was later reported that the bidding did not reach the reserve price and the lot was withdrawn.

Four years later the mill was again advertised for sale and was purchased by Moses and Aaron Burton for the sum of £1,500. The firm was renamed shortly after as Moses Burton & Co, and continued milling until Moses died in 1905. The subsequent sale particulars referred to other properties owned by him, including a bakery and confectionary shop on the site and the Beach Bakery at nearby Eastbourne.

1906 saw a major change in the method of producing flour at the mill. The Horsebridge Roller Milling Company removed some of the traditional drive machinery and installed a Turner 2-sack plant system that could be driven by either water or steam. The large diameter low breast waterwheel was assisted by a 35hp high pressure condensing engine when required, both of which individually provided ample power. As the mill was set across the free-flowing Cuckmere River, the owners would only use the expensive steam engine if the water level was low, or increased production was required. Despite a fire that destroyed some of the roller milling machinery in January 1908, the company continued here until 1922, when the well-known milling firm McDougalls took over the running of the mill.

The water supply from the Cuckmere River must have been more than adequate, as the old waterwheel was completely overhauled in 1939, according to an inspection carried out of the mill in that year. Some five years later the mill ceased working using the waterwheel, but continued until August 1969 using electricity.

It cannot be said that Horsebridge Mill is in any way an attractive mill, despite its semi-rural location. It is of four floors of brick, with a wooden-built hoisting lucomb at the front. The shape of the original mill is still visible, despite the construction of an extension built upwards through the roof and an incongruous six-storey addition on the south side of the building. There are also a number of one- and two-storey extensions dotted around which give the mill a rather cluttered appearance overall.

The external iron low breast waterwheel, 17ft in diameter by 8ft 10in wide, is the only remaining piece of machinery in or outside the mill. The wheel, following its overhaul in 1939, is still in a reasonably good condition but will surely rust away in time. Odd pieces of the rack and pinion sluice gate remain, but the old leat is now completely silted up.

Horsebridge Mill was a large no-nonsense commercial flour mill, whose owners were never slow to upgrade its power source, using steam engines and later electricity to produce flour. The Cuckmere River still meanders through the site, and while the mill is still occupied further structural deterioration should not take place.

MICHELHAM PRIORY MILL *Upper Dicker*
River Cuckmere TQ 558 093 — Within the grounds of Michelham Priory.

Michelham Priory was established here by Augustinian monks in the 13th century. The Priory later became a farmhouse after the dissolution of the monasteries in 1536 and, although the building has been extended over the years, it still remains a most imposing structure.

A watermill was certainly in existence here in 1434, according to an agreement made between the Prior and the Abbot of Battle. However, during a visit by the Bishop in 1478 the mill was described as 'ruinous'.

Although this is an ancient mill site, the existing building is just one of several that must have occupied the same site, as it was common practice to rebuild just the mill, with any sound materials being re-used. The main timber framing at this mill is oak and reputedly dates from the 16th century, but there is also some early stonework still visible. The existing mill is a standard construction commonly found throughout Sussex, with brick to the first floor and weatherboarding above under a tile roof. When the mill was restored in 1972 an external wooden breastshot clasp arm waterwheel was fitted, with the water controlled by a pentrough, which bears the inscription 'John Upfield & Sons — Catsfield 1890 Battle'.

During the 19th century and the early parts of the 20th century the mill was occupied by a succession of millers, none of whom appeared to stay for any length of time, according to entries in the local trade directories: 1834 — Thomas Child, 1886 — George Thorpe, 1874 — Thomas Brown, 1887 — Henry Brown, 1899 — Ernest Ball, 1911 — George Dann. Commercial milling ceased here in 1924, with the machinery being removed soon after and the empty building then being used as a farm store. A turbine was installed in the mill race to drive a generator to make electricity for the main house and this was still in use in July 1939.

In 1971 the Priory committee decided to restore the mill to working order and, subsequently, the roof was completely retiled and the repair of the interior woodwork was carried out by volunteer labour. Attempts were made to obtain machinery from a disused watermill in West Sussex, but when this failed the appropriate machinery was made over the following three years. The main upright shaft was created from an elm tree, while the french burr millstones came from a disused Suffolk mill and the round wooden stone covers came from the famous Bishopstone Tide Mill near Newhaven.

The mill is now in a sorry state (March 1996) and works no more due to problems relating to the misalignment of the pit wheel and wallower. The wooden waterwheel, seemingly too narrow, the sluice controls and most of the machinery are to be replaced. A grant from the National Lottery of £42,000 has ensured that the replacement work can be carried out during the summer of 1996.

Before disaster struck here, the mill ground flour on a regular basis (much of it being used by the Priory's own baker and restaurant) and it is hoped that this will resume on completion of the repair work.

SESSINGHAM MILL *Arlington*

Tributary to River Cuckmere TQ 541 082 — At Sessingham Farm northwest of Arlington.

This is another watermill that disappeared many years ago. Previously there had been a fulling mill here, but the last mill was of the farmer's-own-use type, although it had millstones. This was confirmed when the sale advertisement appeared in the *Sussex Advertiser* of 1 October 1827:

'To be sold by private contract. Sessingham Farm situated at Arlington, consisting of a brick mill house, recently erected, two barns, a watermill to thrash and grind corn on a most excellent construction. Apply to Mr Skinner, Alfriston, who will show the estate.'

Nothing now exists even to indicate the position of the site, although Sessingham Farm remains and a small tributary of the Cuckmere River passes through the site.

Twissell's Mill in 1899. (CW)

74

ABOVE: Horam Mill lay disused in July 1961. (TD) BELOW: The
wooden wagon shed prominent at Hellingly Mill.

ABOVE: Hellingly Mill was used as tea rooms in 1938. (VE) BELOW:
Hellingly Mill from the road in 1991.

ABOVE: The front entrance to Horsebridge Mill in 1991. BELOW:
Stream Mill was used as a chicken feed store in 1941. (AS)

ABOVE: Horsebridge Mill in 1939 with an assortment of building extensions, (AS) and BELOW: in use as an engineering factory in 1991.

78

ABOVE: The wooden waterwheel (now dismantled) at BELOW: the
(restored) Michelham Priory Mill in 1991.

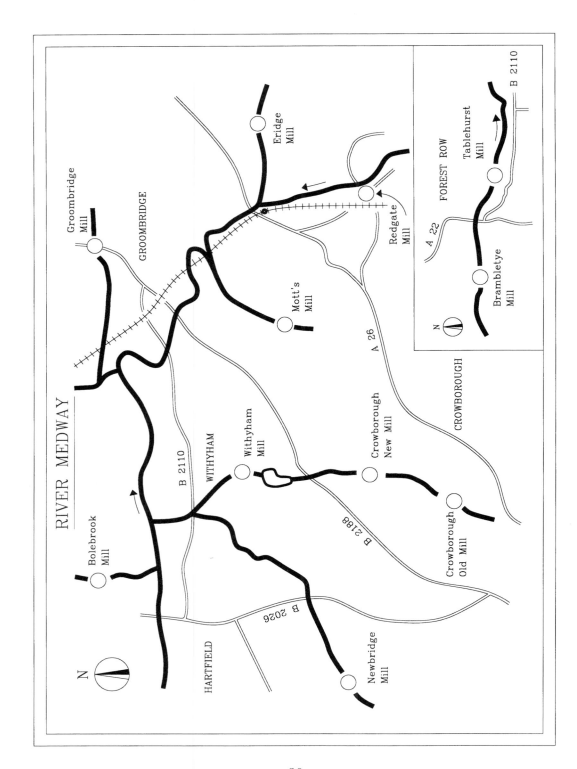

RIVER MEDWAY

Bolebrook Mill

HARTFIELD

B 2026

B 2110

Newbridge Mill

B 2188

WITHYHAM

Withyham Mill

Crowborough New Mill

Crowborough Old Mill

Groombridge Mill

GROOMBRIDGE

Mott's Mill

Eridge Mill

Redgate Mill

A 26

CROWBOROUGH

FOREST ROW

A 22

Brambletye Mill

Tablehurst Mill

B 2110

RIVER MEDWAY

BRAMBLETYE MILL *Forest Row*
River Medway TQ 416 355 — At end of private track south of Lewes Road.

It is very rare to visit a mill site and find absolutely nothing left to indicate its exact position. One such instance is Brambletye Mill, located just to the west of Forest Row. According to Straker, the mill stopped working by waterpower in September 1936 but, since its demolition, extensive regrading of the river bank has taken place and all traces of the mill site have completely disappeared.

This is certainly a Domesday mill site and later, in the 17th century, a forge was constructed nearby. The mill was located close to the site of an ancient moated mansion and the ruined turrets of Brambletye House.

The last mill was constructed in a style found commonly in south-east England, that is, brick and timber. It contained 3-pairs of stones and was powered by a wooden overshot waterwheel, with iron banding, which was positioned in an arched covered extension forming part of the building at its west end. The last mill here was partly rebuilt in 1866 following a fire that destroyed most of the mill.

During the collation of the Defence Schedules in 1803 the mill was occupied by William Durrant, and he continued to at least 1823, with his widow carrying on until 1826. The Tithe Apportionment of 1843 refers to Richard Sisley as the occupier but, soon after, James Dickinson was the miller, remaining until 1859 when he in turn was followed by James and Harriet Mellish from the milling family at Edenbridge Mill. Charles Holmden, previously the miller at Scarletts' Mill and Haxted Mill, took over and ran the mill in partnership with his sons until 1927. From 1930 until at least 1938 the mill was in control of Dickson & Church, who later ran the large Isfield Mill in conjunction.

According to an inspection of the mill in 1945 it was still working, using a tractor to turn the machinery following problems with the waterwheel, which apparently kept slipping off its axle shaft. The reason for the demolition of the mill in 1968 is unclear.

The 1873 Ordnance Survey 25in map of the area depicts a 'Seed Mill' just upstream of the corn mill, on a millpond embankment. Little is known about the mill, but among the sale particulars of the Brambletye estate in November 1865 mention is made of a well-built and substantial watermill with an overshot waterwheel driving 3-pairs of stones, and of a seed mill.

Both mills were on a long leat cut from the River Medway, but have now passed into obscurity.

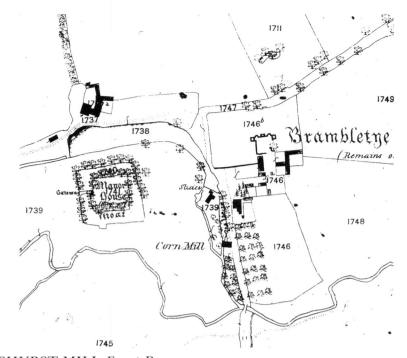

TABLESHURST MILL *Forest Row*

River Medway TQ 433 353 — At the end of a farm track northeast of Forest Row.

The disappearance of Tablehurst Mill is complete and now only the stagnant water in the former tumbling bay marks the site. According to Straker, writing in the *Sussex County Magazine* in June 1932, the original mill was known as 'Dicker's Mill' and was located east of the Forest Row railway station (before it was rebuilt at its present site). This suggestion appeares to be pure conjecture, as the last mill here was of fairly ancient construction and would certainly, in age, have preceded the East Grinstead to Tunbridge Wells railway built in 1866. Straker may have been confused by the extensive alterations to the leat to accommodate the new railway line.

According to the Defence Schedules of 1803, Edward Heaver was the miller, and he continued until 1832, after which the mill passed into the control of the Turner family until at least 1913, with Richard, Robert and finally John the subsequent millers. By the latter years of the 19th century the mill was generally in decline and only producing animal feed. After lying derelict for many years it was finally pulled down in 1946.

Tablehurst Mill was built in the typical style, with brick to the first floor and tarred weatherboarding above. Old photographs of the mill, taken at the turn of the century, show one external clasp arm waterwheel. Kenneth Reid, writing in his book *Watermills of the London Countryside Vol. 1*, states that there were two waterwheels here working in tandem, and a drawing by the author in 1932 shows two wheel axles, bereft of arms, protruding from the pit floor wall.

This was a medium-size watermill that in its latter days utilised 3-pairs of stones. The mill formed part of the bay, with the water provided by a leat (virtually an elongated millpond) that branched off the main river south of a property known as 'Tablehurst' some 400 yards west of the mill. The old miller's cottage on higher ground to the north of the mill site is the only tangible relic connected with this mill.

NEWBRIDGE MILL *Coleman's Hatch*
Tributary to River Medway TQ 456 328 — Adjacent to a minor road south-east of Coleman's Hatch.

Newbridge Mill was constructed in the late 18th century, located in an open valley in the Ashdown Forest.

Although there was a corn mill here from at least 1497, the immediate surrounding area was used in conjunction with the iron industry, with Simon Ballarde producing large quantities of iron shot here. Later, in 1574, Henry Bowyer (the Queen's Ironmaster in the Forest) was in control of two large furnaces, but by 1650 the ironworks had been abandoned and the area eventually returned to its quieter rural seclusion. Nothing more is known about the early mills here, until one is mentioned in the Parliamentary Survey of 1658 when it was referred to as 'the watermill at Newbridge within the Forest'.

During the 19th and early 20th centuries, *Kelly's* trade directories list four different millers here. James and George Fillery were millers here in 1866, being followed by William Bellingham and, in 1895, Edwin West. He in turn was followed by Albert Edwards, the last working miller. The 1932 Ordnance Survey 6in map records the site as a 'Corn Mill' but by this time the mill had ceased working commercially. In its latter working days an external pulley wheel, its axle still protruding through the weatherboarding, was a relic of the times when a traction engine would supplement deficiencies in the water supply.

When the top floor of the mill was converted into an annexe for the house all the internal machinery was removed. Records show that Newbridge Mill was a 3-pair mill, finally having two burrs and one peakstone, and at the back of the mill is a medium-size millpond (although alterations have been carried out, reducing it in size). The extant 'waterwheel', if it can be called that, is made of glass fibre and similar in shape to a barrel (it defies further description). Apparently, it was installed soon after the mill was converted and was connected to a generator.

The mill has three floors, one brick and two weatherboarding, and is kept in good order. There is a small extension, set on brick piers, on the east side of the building set over the pentrough, through which the water still pours. At the entrance to the mill lies the discarded remains of the pitwheel (approximately 7ft 6in in diameter).

The mill forms part of a group of distinguished buildings, all at one time connected with it, and there is a steep incline to the road above.

BOLEBROOK MILL *Hartfield*
Tributary to River Medway TQ 481 374 — At the end of lane east of the B2026 one mile north of Hartfield.

The mill stands at the end of a lane on the east side of the Hartfield to Edenbridge road. A mill on this site is mentioned in the Domesday Book, when the rent was quoted as '4s and 250 eels'.

The mill forms part of an attractive group of buildings set into the millpond embankment and includes the mill house, much enlarged over the years, and the miller's barn, predominantly used for storage. The mill itself is of three floors, with white painted weatherboarding above the ground floor of dressed stone. A white painted lucomb at the front gives the mill a smart appearance.

The present mill dates from 1740, but some of the dressed stone is of a much earlier period. Until 1977 the mill possessed a large diameter wooden clasp arm oak waterwheel, 11ft by 5ft 6in wide. Alas, during a violet storm the wheel was so badly damaged that it had to be dismantled and the old wooden axle shaft, with iron winged gudgeons, now protrudes rather sadly out of the mill over an empty wheelpit. Water was fed into the millpond by way of a long headrace connected to the River Medway, while further water was provided from a catchment area to the north of the mill. Straker, writing in the *Sussex County Magazine* of August 1939, infers that there was another large pond upstream of the millpond, all traces of which have disappeared.

Henry Atherfold was the miller here in 1845, he being replaced by his brother John, who continued until 1865 after which John Burfoot took over. Burfoot remained at the mill until 1899, when Alfred Tester took over. The mill continued working full time until 1931 and occasionally for some years after, with the Tester family in occupation until its closure.

Inside the mill the great majority of the drive machinery remains and on the stone floor above are the remains of a pair of peak millstones, together with the crown wheel that once drove, via shafting, a water pump on the other wide of the wheel pit. A hole had to be cut into the weatherboarding to allow access for the necessary belt drive.

Some 30 years ago the deteriorating condition of the mill gave little hope for its future. However, the present owners have ensured that the mill, house and associated barns are kept in an excellent condition and visitors can avail themselves of a meticulously run bed and breakfast accommodation.

CROWBOROUGH NEW MILL *Crowborough*
Tributary to River Medway TQ 489 304 — Southwest of Marden's Hill, one and a quarter miles northwest of Crowborough.

A cursory glance at the site of Crowborough New Mill would seemingly indicate the existence of just another demolished watermill. Nothing could be further from the truth, as there is more to this site than is first apparent.

The mill site is to be found on St John's Common, a mixture of woodland and open heathland through which flows a tributary of the River Medway. The tributary was ponded at five separate locations to provide water power for the two watermills situated here.

Edward Howis, who was a London-based dealer in vegetable oil and owner of a large shipping business based in Piccadilly, purchased the lease of the Crowborough Lodge estate in 1809. The estate was given its present name shortly afterwards and totalled 1,700 acres. Howis used the property as an investment and cleared much of the scrub heathland, planting various hardwoods for timber and coppicing. Perhaps his biggest investment was the construction of a large watermill positioned just to the south of the old iron furnace bay. He dammed two ponds at the site, with a combined surface area of 10 acres, the lower of which had a massive embankment of over 35ft. Howis then set up an extensive flour trade from this mill and at the Old Mill situated to the south. As Howis was a dealer in vegetable oil it could be presumed that the mill was erected for that purpose, though there is no evidence to support this. Howis died in 1830, but the mill that he erected became well-known for grinding the flour for Queen Victoria's wedding cake in 1840. Howis's widow, Charlotte, carried on using the mill until at least

1843, according to the Tithe Apportionment. Thereafter, the mill continued to be used in conjunction with the Old Mill, according to *Kelly's* trade directories. John Carpenter took over from Charlotte Howis but was replaced by Walasby & Feltham in 1855. The last occupiers were Richard Marchant, from 1870, then, finally, Charles Colbran, from 1903, when Crowborough Mill was recorded as being steam assisted. It is not known for how long the mill continued working, but the building was semi-ruinous by the 1920s, according to Straker. Sidney Ashdown, writing in August 1947, described it as a fine mill, substantially built, with each floor supported by iron moulded pillars. The large waterwheel had been removed for scrap during the war and he also commented upon the fact that, at the time, the top pond was drained and the lower partially drained.

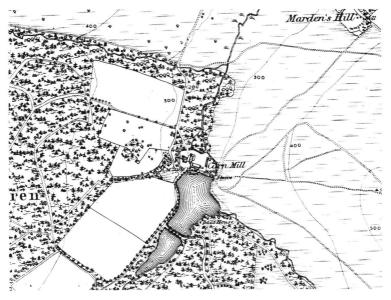

The whole layout of the site was completely altered in 1949 when, following prolonged rainfall, the pond embankment collapsed and water from the two large millponds tore through the site. The mill building lay disused and open to the elements until 1968, when the mill was demolished for its building stone which was, apparently, of exceptional quality. The position of the mill and the elaborate and extensive watercourses were by no means of a standard layout or design.

It is certainly common in south-east England for an 'overshot' watermill to form part of the pond embankment, and why this was not the arrangement here is obscure. In the event, a rather complicated system was installed to bring the water some 50 yards from the pond to the waterwheel. A small adjustable cover plate was built into a headwall at the side of the millpond. Water entering this pipe then travelled underground for some 30 yards, emerging into a brick-built open box channel that eventually turned at right angles towards the mill. It was then carried along an aqueduct to the watermill, most of which was enclosed within the mill itself. The waterwheel was approximately 33ft in diameter and would have been a slow turning wheel. The tail water from the wheel was carried away in a bricklined tunnel to rejoin the main river some 40 yards away. The pond overflow was of ornate construction, with brick archways and a stepped weir, and just took water when it reached the appropriate height. There was another overflow sluice at the other end of the pond embankment, but following the flood of 1949 this disappeared without trace.

The mill was built in the grand style with its dressed stone under a large tiled roof, which had a wooden lucomb. It contained at least 3-pairs of stones, counter geared (for such a well-established mill, little further technical information exists). One of the features of this site was the number of associated buildings here. The 1873 Ordnance Survey 25in map clearly shows three other buildings apart from the mill. It has not been possible to identify the long thin building running northwards from the base of the pond embankment, but old postcard views have identified the other two buildings. One building was situated on the top of the embankment and appeared to function for storage and possibly accommodation, while the other was a two-storey house built in a deep hollow opposite the front of the mill, with its roof barely above the level of the access track that passed by. This building must have been very susceptible to damp and had gone by 1910. Also at the same time, on the Ordnance Survey map, vegetation had started to grow in the lower millpond, which appears to indicate that the mill was not working full time, or had even stopped.

In the summer months the site is enveloped in vegetation, but winter reveals much more. Following the collapse of the pond embankment in 1949, extensive regrading of the site took place. The hollow, where the house stood, has been filled in, and the stream runs through the middle of the site. The brick arched overflow and stepped weir still remain, as does a rather peculiar concrete box standing where the pond was. This box enabled the pond to be drained quickly through an access channel, which no longer exists. Descending to the site of the mill, one of the stone-bearing blocks for the axle shaft of the waterwheel still remains *in situ*. The stone footings of the engine house are next to the filled-up wheel pit, which indicates that during its latter working days water supply was surprisingly a problem. Other stone footings indicate the outline of the mill itself, while the tail water tunnel is now well buried and untraceable. The brick-built open box culvert remains, but the aqueduct no longer exists. It would appear that when the mill was dismantled for its stone in 1968 any remaining standing features were destroyed, and the site has since become overgrown. Near to the mill site is a small arched bridge that carried the track that once passed the front of the mill. The present footpath to the west of the site, although shown on old maps, was in no way associated with access to the mill. It is quite remarkable how the landscape of a site can change so completely but, fortunately, there is an abundance of postcard views of the mill which help us to appreciate the size and layout of this important mill site.

CROWBOROUGH OLD MILL *Crowborough*
Tributary to River Medway TQ 487 302 — Located at Old Mill Farm, one and a quarter miles west of Crowborough.

The Old Mill site lies in an isolated position to the east of Crowborough Warren, part of which is an established woodland through which a stream rises and flows through to the River Medway at Withyham. A fair-sized iron furnace was working here in the Warren in the 17th century, the stream being ponded in several places accordingly. The pond bay, for the furnace downstream, can still be found, but the Old Mill was set up below the highest of the ponds.

The 1900 Ordnance Survey 6in map, shows this mill to be an unusually long building. There remains some doubt as to the age of this mill site, but it would be reasonable to assume that it was established here by Edward Howis, who leased the large estate in 1809. Howis was also responsible for erecting the larger and more prestigious New Mill futher downstream. When Howis's widow Charlotte sold the mill in 1844 it was bought by the Ramsbottom family, who leased the mill to several millers up until the end of the century. However, an inspection of the local trade directories reveals few references to the mill, suggesting that it was not in general trade.

The mill building was still standing in 1908 but, following a disastrous fire, it was reduced to ruins by 1929 and there is nothing of the mill to be seen today. Curiously, to the north of the mill site are the distinct remains of a pond bay, complete with brick arched bridge — perhaps a survivor from a previous mill site.

There are also records to suggest that the Old Mill building was converted into a saw mill in its latter days, but these are not accurate. Close to the millpond enbankment are to be found the ruins of a small dressed-stone building, from which protrude an iron pipe and box pentrough. Below this are the unmistakable remains of a wheelpit, and this was the saw mill referred to earlier. A contemporary photograph shows an assortment of buildings here. Vegetation has now completely overgrown the site and, along with the semi-derelict farm buildings, it forms a most dismal scene. The mill house still survives, although largely altered over the years, and is on strictly private property.

WITHYHAM MILL *Withyham*
Tributary to River Medway TQ 496 356 — In the grounds of Buckhurst Park estate.

This important and ancient mill site is now little more than a memory. A mill is shown on the Buckhurst Terrier in 1598 in the tenancy of John Pulman, for a rental of £100. Earlier, in 1574, the area supported a forge, but it is not clear whether the corn mill worked in conjunction with this or whether the mill referred to on the Terrier was a new mill.

Surprisingly, very little is known about the mill other than that the tenants here between 1843 and 1882 were Thomas Caffyn, John Homewood and Alfred Hall respectively. Although the ornamental waters in the estate were enlarged as part of a major landscaping project in the 1830s, the mill is known to have survived this disruption, and was marked accordingly on the 1874 Ordnance Survey 25in map.

Following the demise of the mill towards the end of the 19th century, a small one-floor brick building was erected on the site of the mill. This building houses an internal waterwheel, 8ft in diameter, and three water pumps. However, this building has fallen into total disrepair and stands neglected and disused amongst a mass of tangled undergrowth.

REDGATE MILL *Rotherfield*
Eridge Stream — tributary to River Medway TQ 552 325 — By an unclassified road one mile north of Rotherfield.

Redgate Mill does not stand on an ancient site and the present structure is, most probably, the only mill to have existed here. The mill is tucked away from the more populated areas and probably served the local farming community and the immediate locality.

Redgate Mill was never a large corn mill and possible had 3-pairs of stones, with its motive power being supplied by an overshot waterwheel which, like all of the internal machinery, was removed when the mill stopped working at the turn of the century.

After its closure it was named Redgate Mill Farm, as shown on the 1910 Ordnance Survey 6in map and the mill was used thereafter as a store, forming part of the farm outbuildings.

According to the Defence Schedules of 1803, Ann Wickens was the occupier of the mill at that time, and it remained in the occupation of Charles Wickens for some time after, with William Coad the last miller here, in 1895.

The mill has three floors, with tarred weatherboarding on top of a dressed-stone base under a tiled roof. Some years ago the mill was converted to a house of some style. To commemorate its past, half a wooden dummy 'waterwheel' was built over the wheelpit!

The former mill building is to be found just to the east of the Uckfield railway line, at a point where the disused railway line to Mayfield once branched off.

ERIDGE MILL *Eridge*

Eridge Stream — tributary to River Medway TQ 564 350 — Situated beside to Mill Wood in Eridge Park.

The site of Eridge Mill lies in open countryside some 1½ miles east of Eridge. There is a large pond in Eridge Park of a size appropriate for the iron industry: a furnace was in operation here in 1567, as corroborated by Budgeon, who marks the site as 'Furnace' on his map published in 1724.

There is little other information given about the mill, apart that from that noted by Greenwood, who marks the site (with no symbol) on his map of 1823/4. Previous to this, the mill was recorded in the Defence Schedules of 1803, when the miller, Henry Slatter, was reportedly willing to supply two sacks of flour daily (using his own wheat) in time of invasion. The mill had gone by 1846, according to the Tithe Apportionments, probably due to its isolated position.

It is now difficult to identify the site but beside a public right of way that runs southeast from Eridge Green and next to Mill Wood can be seen the unmistakable remains of a low pond embankment. This former millpond is now completely overgrown and devoid of any other remains of the mill.

MOTT'S MILL *Withyham*

Tributary to River Medway TQ 523 353 — Next to side road in Mott's Mill, south of Groombridge.

The search for the site of Mott's Mill is not difficult, as a small community has adopted and preserved the name of the mill. However, identifying the actual site of the former flour mill is a different matter.

The district of Mott's Mill lies nestled in a small valley and is reached by a minor road that diverges northeast from the B2188 that continues into Groombridge. As the mill was tucked away from the more popular routes in the district, information and comment about the mill is sparse, to say the least.

Mott's Mill appears to have gone by 1724 (the date of Budgeon's map), although a mill was in existence here towards the end of the 16th century, according to the Buckhurst Terrier map. In a report in the 1930s reference was made to the existence of a waterfall, together with a sluice gate, but even these features appear to have gone, leaving just the faint outline of a small pond bay as a possible indication of the site.

GROOMBRIDGE MILL *Groombridge*
River Grom — tributary to River Medway TQ 531 376 — Beside B2188, west of Groombridge Place.

Groombridge Mill is a picturesque building that, along with the adjoining 17th-century mill house, forms a most pleasing group. The mill lies at the bottom of the hill in the grounds of Groombridge Place, a building of great antiquity barely inside the Kent boundary. The external fabric of the mill is kept in good condition by the estate, thus ensuring its survival to the present, and for many years to come.

Groombridge was a small mill containing, in its latter working days, 2-pairs of stones. It has a tile roof with tile hung upper walls, complemented by the use of local brickwork and sandstone masonry. There is an outside door to the ground floor, with another similar door to the first floor. The inside is unusual in that although of three floors the mill is open from the ground floor to the stone floor, as a section of the wooden 'stone floor' has been cut away.

It is not known whether this is an ancient mill site, but a close inspection of the lower walls of the ground floor reveals a structure of 16th-century origin, or earlier. The existing mill was therefore probably just a rebuild on old foundations. Power to the mill was provided by the River Grom, which was ponded here when comprehensive landscaping was carried out for Groombridge Place in the 18th century. The millpond was formed and the dam heightened to provide more power to an overshot waterwheel. The tail race from the mill passed by the side of the mill house in a tunnel, went under the road and then had to make two right-angled turns to rejoin the river, which, in effect, annexed the mill to Kent and the waterwheel to Sussex. This tail race no longer exists, though traces of it are still to be seen, and there is no sign of the waterwheel, pentrough or feed from the millpond.

The mill contains some superb wooden machinery and has other features to enthuse about. The wooden upright shaft was driven by the pit wheel and wallower, which are the only parts of the drive machinery made of iron. The 8ft 4in diameter wooden spur wheel has just four radial arms, but is in very poor condition. There are also *in situ* two wooden stone nuts, with removable cogs, and a superbly crafted wooden crown wheel, which drove a wooden-shafted idler pulley sack hoist and oat crusher. There are two bedstones *in situ* on the stone floor — one peak and one french burr, the latter being only 34in in diameter. There are also the remains of a wire machine and a rather odd-looking peg and lever system that no doubt operated the pentrough gate. Also, there is a governor that operated off the upright shaft, corn scales and a meal scoop. As the mill worked through to as late as 1934 it is unusual that cast iron machinery had not been installed, but fortunately, for the mill enthusiast, it is rewarding to see so much wooden machinery *in situ* (most of it in good condition).

From at least 1826 until 1866 the Durrant family were in control of the mill, with Amos taking over from John. Amos Durrant was described as a bankrupt, according to the *London Gazette* of 6 April 1862, he being replaced by James Sumner. Abraham Betchley and Caleb Russell were two further millers here, but after 1905 the mill probably reverted to being an estate mill, grinding provender feed until its final closure.

OPPOSITE ABOVE: The impressive Brambletye Mill, photographed
in 1961, tragically burnt down in 1968. (FG) CENTRE: Tablehurst Mill
in 1907; now only the house remains, (RP) and BELOW: in a poor state
of repair in 1910. (RP) ABOVE: Newbridge Mill in May 1939 (AS) and
BELOW: in the landscape in 1928.

91

ABOVE: The attractive Bolebrook Mill in 1991, BELOW: now an award-winning bed and breakfast accommodation.

ABOVE: The large and impressive Crowborough New Mill, and
BELOW: The mill house set well below the mill. (both VE)

ABOVE: The aqueduct and waterwheel at Crowborough New Mill, now sadly gone. (VE) BELOW: Redgate Mill was in use as a farm store in May 1939. (AS)

ABOVE: Wooden machinery and BELOW: A rare wooden stone nut, at
Groombridge Mill in 1991.

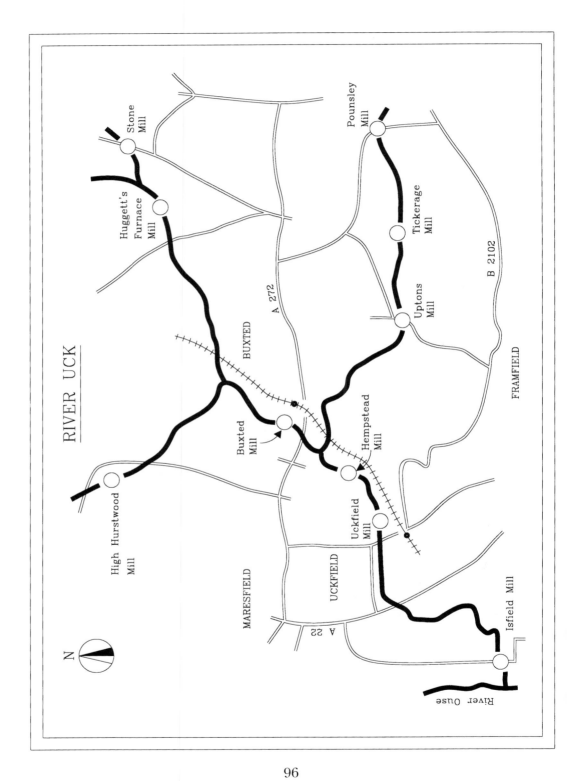

RIVER UCK

STONE MILL *Rotherfield*
Tributary to River Uck TQ 543 265 — On the east side of Rotherfield road towards Hadlow Down.

Stone Mill was converted into a house in 1954 and can be seen beside a steep and narrow lane two miles south of Rotherfield.

This is certainly an ancient site, with a reference as early as 1535, when it formed part of a family settlement on the Hadlow Down estate. In 1584 the mill was in the possession of the Goldsmith family but later, in 1673, Adam Goldsmith was found guilty of deliberately letting the mill fall into disrepair, after which he quickly sold the mill to Anthony Cole. That was not the end of disputes at this time, as Cole later had to pay 5s compensation for 'overthrowing the mill house', and it would appear that the mill was rebuilt at this time.

John Ashby became the occupier and then the owner of the mill from 1782 until 1856, with his son Charles continuing for a short time. Ashby had purchased the mill following a sale advertisement that appeared in the *Sussex Weekly Advertiser* of 20 October 1794. William Wilmshurst was the next occupier, he in turn being followed by Eli Dadswell, the last miller at the mill. In his relatively short time at the mill, Dadswell fitted a new pair of millstones and refitted the overshot waterwheel. Dadswell worked the mill in conjunction with Huggett's Furnace Mill until 1896, when he was made bankrupt, according to an entry in the *London Gazette*. So ended centuries of flour and animal feed production at Stone Mill and it joined a growing list of working watermills that did not survive into the 20th century.

Stone Mill is a small Grade II listed three-storey building built of brick and timber with white weatherboarding dating from the 18th century, with the mill house attached to it on its northern side. After the mill ceased working, a turbine was fitted to provide electricity, with the site being marked on the 1911 Ordnance Survey 6in map as 'Stone Mill (electric light works)'.

In 1949 sale particulars stated that electricity was formerly supplied from the private electric plant housed in the timber and tiled building adjoining the road (this refers to the disused mill building).

Stone Mill is set in a quiet and peaceful corner of Sussex, amongst countryside unaltered for centuries.

HUGGETT'S FURNACE MILL *Hadlow Down*
River Uck TQ 534 260 — Beside a farm track north of Hadlow Down.

Huggett's Furnace Mill is located in a secluded position reached by a winding narrow lane. It is set within a group of farm outbuildings, including an oast-house, but the mill site is now totally devoid of live water. The mill has recently been converted into a house but, while there is always concern when mills are 'modernised', in this instance without such work the building would surely have collapsed. As early as February 1939 Sidney Ashdown recorded that the mill was in a deplorable state, so its conversion will ensure that the mill building at least survives.

The mill stands near, or on, the site of a once important iron mill, and Straker records in 1931 that (according to Lower) the first iron guns manufactured in Sussex were cast here, in 1543. At some time after, when iron production ceased in the middle of the 17th century, a corn mill and a saw mill were erected to make use of the existing ponded water, although because of silting a smaller pond was added at a later date.

Huggett's Furnace Mill is a brick and timber buiding of three floors that ceased working in 1923/4, although it appears to have last worked on a regular basis in 1909. It was latterly used as a store for the farm and at the time of its closure all the internal machinery was cleared out. The wooden axle shaft still exists and resting against a wall is a millstone, which bears the inscription 'F W 1773'. Huggett's Furnace Mill was only a small 2-pair mill that was ultimately, towards the end of the 19th century, used to produce animal feed — although it was marked as 'Corn' on the 1874 Ordnance Survey 25in map. Throughout the 19th century and until its closure the mill remained under the control of the Dadswell family, with Eli also running Stone Mill, taking over from Edward during the late 1870s. Near to the mill is Huggett's Mill Farm, a Victorian farmhouse of later date than the mill.

HIGH HURSTWOOD MILL *High Hurstwood*
Tributary to River Uck TQ 493 262 — South of village centre.

The mill that served the village of High Hurstwood was small but it worked a good trade over the years and only ceased working following the collapse of a bridge tree support beam in the pit floor. It lies just below a small track carried on an artificial pond bay that leads off the road through the village. It is a Grade II listed building forming part of a small group of buildings, including a mill house of much greater age than the mill. It is difficult to assess the age of the mill, but a date at the beginning of the 19th century is likely. It is built in the traditional style of brick to the first floor with weatherboarding above. Entry into the mill is either by way of an access from the road, directly onto the bin floor, or by a door leading directly into the pit floor at the front of the mill.

Unlike many other mills, High Hurstwood contains most of its machinery, mainly wooden, even though the building has been disused for over 75 years. The framework of the external iron overshot waterwheel, 18ft 6in in diameter by 3ft 3in wide, survives and carries the inscription 'S. Medhurst & Son, September 1867'. It was fed from two half round iron pipes and developed 10hp. Inside the ground floor of the mill the pit wheel, of the few pieces of iron machinery, is 8ft in diameter and connects with an iron wallower. The remaining machinery is wooden, with the crown wheel (4ft 6in in diameter) being of the cross arm type, morticed directly onto the upright shaft. The crown wheel drove seemingly complicated sack hoist machinery, while on the west side 8of the building a drive was taken off to operate a dresser and kibbler. Lower down the upright shaft the spur wheel turned 2-pairs of millstones, one french burr and one peak (3ft 10in and 4ft diameter respectively).

98

The first recorded occupier was John Duvall, who was replaced by Killick Kenward in 1858. Later, in 1874, Kenward was recorded in partnership with Mr Noakes, and so things continued until 1890, when John Hoath took over the mill. In 1905 the mill was leased by Edwin Brown, who stayed in occupation until the mill stopped working in 1920 — though in its latter working days it was just producing chicken feed.

There do not appear to exist any records to indicate the existence of an earlier mill on this site, which is rather surprising as the early 17th-century mill house is of great antiquity while the former millpond, on the other side of the causeway, is nothing more than a tangled mass of vegetation, with little evidence of standing water.

The present owner has spent a considerable amount of time and money on the mill over the last 25 years — but further expense will be required soon, especially with regard to the floor boarding on the stone floor, which is in a rather precarious state to say the least!

According to the Tithe Apportionment in the middle of the 19th century, there was another watermill nearby and lower down the stream, but nothing more is known about this venture.

BUXTED MILL *Buxted*

River Uck TQ 494 235 — At the end of a track north of Station Road, a quarter of a mile west of Buxted.

Buxted Mill is a Grade II listed building with brick to the first floor, and two floors of hung slate above. The existing building is a substantial structure of early 19th-century origin, located behind more modern properties fronting Station Road.

The mill had been converted to residential accommodation by 1945 and the internal drive machinery removed. The framework of the external overshot waterwheel remains, its buckets having been either removed or rusted away. The waterwheel is 9ft 6in in diameter by 10ft wide, constructed in cast iron with three sets of arms; it drove 2-pairs of stones. The rack and pinion penstock, with elm boards, still exists and has been restored recently but there is no live water supply running through the site.

The first reference to this mill site dates from 1655, in the form of an indenture of an apprentice to the miller, Thomas Wisborne. The first insurance records provide move information, especially in the latter half of the 18th century. In 1785 Edward Brunston, the owner of the mill, insured his water corn mill, timber with a thatched roof. Smith Burley was the mill at this time (in 1794 he is recorded at Maresfield Mill).

John Catt became the proprietor of the new mill, his family being millers at several other watermills in the county — most notable of which was the massive Bishopstone Tide Mills south of Newhaven. Catt stayed at Buxted until at least 1842, after which James Bedford became the miller, continuing until 1868. In this year a curious incident took place between the miller and Colonel Harcourt, who became the owner of the mill soon after. During the period when the mill was advertised for sale, Harcourt, a prospective candidate for the coming elections, called on Bedford to ascertain who he was going to vote for. Bedford replied that he would vote for Harcourt if he bought the mill. What happened afterwards is not clear, but obviously Bedford did not vote as expected as he was turned out of the mill shortly afterwards — much to his disgust!

Ebenezer Warburton took over the mill following Bedford's eviction and remained until 1907, from which date William Wilmshurst took over (he was also the miller at

Barcombe Mills in 1908 and must have found Buxted Mill a rather small mill by comparison). William Bailey, a Buxted corn merchant and baker, was using the mill only on a part-time basis up to November 1939, after which all trade directory references to the mill cease. According to an inspection made in May 1946, the mill had closed down in the early days of the war when, for defence purposes, a ditch was cut across this part of the county, thus interfering with the water supply.

POUNSLEY MILL *Blackboys*
Tributary to River Uck TQ 526 218 — In the garden of the Mill House, half a mile north of Blackboys.

In 1619 mention was made to 'Pounslowe Mill' and an iron furnace at Blackboys, all under the ownership of Nicholas Eversfield. According to a rental agreement made at that time the furnace was situated across the stream from the mill, and worked in conjunction with it. It is hard to picture the mill working in an environment of fumes and debris produced by a working iron furnace.

Although the mill is not shown on the 1813 Ordnance Survey 1in map, it was certainly in existence, and in the occupation of Isaac Gurr. Earlier, in 1788, the *Sussex Weekly Advertiser* commented on a tragic accident that occurred at the mill in June of that year:

'A few days since, Mr Buckwell, of Pounsley Mill, in the parish of Framfield, was at work therein, the cogs of one of the wheels caught hold of his frock, and drew his arm in amongst them by which accident his hand received so much injury that he was under the necessity of having it immediately cut off above the wrist.'

A far more pleasant, and remarkable, report appeared in the same paper published in February 1813:

'There is now living in the parish of Framfield a young man, named Joseph Babuck, who although he has been blind since he was a year old, is as capable of performing the business of a Grinder as well as most men who follow that occupation. In the above said parish there are three water corn mills at all which 'Blind Joey' has occasionally been employed; he now officiates at Pounsley Mill, to which most of the grist of the neighbourhood are carried, and committed to the blind man's care, for the purpose of grinding, dressing etc., and all this he executed with the greatest facility and dispatch, even to the discharge of the toll-dish; and will afterwards deliver his grist round the parish with more readiness and accuracy than many who have the advantage of sight. He forms a wheat stack with a degree of neatness peculiar to himself, and never loses sight of that employment during the harvest months. His celebrity as a country dance player in the village, gives him the lead of all the fashionable hops of the neighbourhood parishes, which he visits on most merry occasions, but never takes with him a guide.'

Isaac Gurr was made bankrupt in 1820, and from then on it appears that the mill worked in close conjunction with the nearby farm. Edward Norman (1841), Samuel Relf (1845) and, finally, Henry Leney (1855-78) were the recorded occupiers of the mill during the 19th century.

Pounsley Mill was a small three-storey watermill that contained only 2-pairs of stones, built of brick to the first floor with weatherboarding above, all under a tiled roof. The building has been gutted of all machinery and is used as a stable with a children's playroom above. It now stands marooned without purpose and the only clue to its former use is the steep bank, on its east side, where the overshot waterwheel was positioned. Just to the north of the mill is a small depression that was once the millpond, now grassed over. The large pond to the north of the site was used in conjunction with the iron furnace.

TICKERAGE MILL *Blackboys*
River Uck TQ 514 211 — At the bottom of a track northwest of Blackboys.

This is another site established following the demise of the iron industry in Sussex. The site held both a furnace and a forge (though not at the same time) from 1671, with the forge continuing working until 1653.

Tickerage Mill is situated in close proximity to Pounsley Mill and Upton's Mill and care has to be taken when referring to a particular mill, as all three mills were located within the parish of Framfield. The first accurate reference to a corn mill on this site appeared in the Defence Schedules of 1803, when John Smith was the miller. Smith continued to at least 1809, he being followed by Thomas Packham. Edward Dadswell was in occupation by 1851 and it remained in the same family until 1887, with Ebenezer in control, and it was at this time that the mill was recorded as 'steam and water'. The last family to use the mill were the Paris's, with George and John the recorded millers. John Paris continued until just before 1930, after which the mill was closed down. By 1946 the mill was derelict and although it contained its machinery the future was uncertain.

This Grade II listed building dating from the 17th century is set beside a causeway and utilised water from a pond on the other side to power a 14ft diameter iron overshot waterwheel manufactured by Medhurst & Son of Lewes. The mill is built to three storeys of brick and timber and still survives. It is thought that no internal machinery exists, but the owner of the nearby mill house prohibits access. The mill can be seen from a right of way that passes the front door.

The mill is at the bottom of a steep lane that branches off the B2102 in the village of Blackboys and, for the meantime, its future looks secure.

UPTON'S MILL *Framfield*
River Uck TQ 504 212 — On an unclassified road northeast of Framfield.

This is an 18th-century mill site, with the first reference appearing in May 1772, when it was advertised for sale, according to an entry in the *Sussex Weekly Advertiser*. Later, in June 1791, the mill was again advertised for sale, with a notice in the *Sussex Weekly Advertiser* as follows:

'To be sold. A Water Corn Mill known by the name of Upton's Mill, situate in the parish of Framfield, in the occupation of Mr. William Newnham. nb. The above mill is never in want of water, and the hop gardens are remarkable for producing large crops.'

Newnham continued until 1 December 1796, when he was tragically killed after part of his clothing was caught in the machinery and he was crushed to death. The mill remained in the occupation of the Newnham family, as trade directories duly record. By 1855 the mill was owned by Henry Newnham, with George Berry and then William Stevenson the recorded tenants.

The last owner and occupier of the mill was George Heaver, who took over following the death of Henry Newnham in 1874. The sale notice that appeared in the *Sussex Advertiser* of June 1874 provides an insight into the composition of the mill:

'The auctioneers have been instructed by the Trustees to sell by auction under the will of the late Mr. Henry Newnham on 14 July, 1874, at the Star Hotel, Lewes.

Lot 1. A Water Corn Mill and a small productive farm known as Upton's Mill. The mill is well built with heart of oak timber, and in good working order. A new iron water wheel and large iron supplying trough have been fitted in a thoroughly substantial way, at a cost of £150, within the last three years. There are two pairs of wheat and one pair of oat stones. The Lot, which is situate in Framfield, is now let to William Stevenson (whose tenancy will expire on the 29th September next) at a yearly rent of £120.'

George Heaver continued as owner-occupier at the mill until he died here, at the age of 96, in 1930. According to an inspection of the mill in April 1947, the mill was complete, but disused, and its fate was sealed in 1966 when it was completely gutted and turned into a residence. It is thought that the 10ft 6in diameter iron overshot waterwheel was retained, but this had gone by 1970.

Upton's Mill was built on four floors, one brick and the others weatherboarding, with a large lucomb protruding out from the front of the mill. When approaching the site from the south, the early 17th century Grade II mill house has been renamed 'Upton's Mill', while the old mill is now called 'Heaver's Mill'. This is a pleasant group of buildings on a quiet country road connecting Framfield and Buxted.

HEMPSTEAD MILL *Uckfield*
River Uck TQ 484 217 — North of Hempstead Lane, northeast of Uckfield.

The first known reference to a mill here was in 1756 and relates to a fulling mill, with the same trade referred to again in 1771. Gream's map of 1795 refers to it as 'Oil Mill' but by 1806 a cotton mill occupied the site. It is unusual for such a variety of different trades to be carried out in such a short time — there is even a vague reference to a silk mill here as well! The last trade carried out was flour milling, established here in 1838, and continued to the end of the mill's working life.

As well as appearing in Gream's map, the lease of the oil mill was advertised in the *Sussex Weekly Advertiser* in November 1875, as follows:

'Oil mills. To leather dressers and fellmongers. To be let. An old accustomed Oil Mill, Yards, Pits etc, for dressing of leather in Oil or Allum, together with a dwelling house and garden, situate in the town of Uckfield.'

The oil mill lease was not taken up, for it was converted to a cotton wick mill shortly afterwards. The conversion of the mill to flour milling had been completed by 1838, as a sale advertisement of the cotton machinery appeared a year later. There were several millers working here during the 19th century and it worked in conjunction, quite naturally, with Uckfield Mill in the town centre. Also, at times, it worked with Upton's Mill, at Framfield, and Buxted Mill, with Ebenezer Warburton the last recorded owner (according to a trade directory published in 1937).

Inside this Grade II listed mill quite a lot of the machinery remains, especially in the pit floor. The frame of the internal 16ft diameter low breastshot survives and appears to be in fairly good structural condition. Three sets of double doors give plenty of access to the wheel. The pit machinery is enclosed and, like the waterwheel, is in good condition. It is arranged in the standard layout, with the 7ft diameter spur wooden wheel of special interest. This is cross-armed, with a plain rim and wooden teeth, morticed directly onto the upright shaft. This wheel is obviously original and throughout the mill there is a combination of new and old machinery. Other unusual features include the governor, worked by a collar attached to the upright shaft, and the wooden spur wheel, which overlaps the top of the waterwheel by 12in. The mill contained 3-pairs of stones, two peak and one burr, with the latter complete and the former bedstones only. The wooden upright shaft is strengthened by six cast iron banding hoops at its base, but has been replaced by a cast iron section from the stone floor upwards to complement the fairly modern iron crown wheel and ancillary drive shafting. The mill ended its days producing electricity, thus ensuring the good condition of the extant machinery.

Hempstead Mill is a fine four-floor mill built of brick and timber with tile hung slate (similar to Buxted Mill) on the first and second floor at the front of the mill. The neighbouring mill house, set at right angles to the mill, is older and was obviously erected for a former industry here.

At one time the mill would have stood alone in the watermeadows of the River Uck, but the site is now on the edge of the expanding town of Uckfield and it is possible that it will be enclosed by housing development some time in the future. The mill and house once formed a small community, with nearby stables and storage areas, while at the east side of the mill is a small brick-built extension that once housed some form of machinery. The mill lies to the north of an unmade road and once must have been an idyllic site before the encroachment of housing development.

The future of the mill looks secure and it is partly used as an office, though this detracts little from its atmosphere. The River Uck still thunders through the bypass to the east of the mill, but the mill leat has been filled in for some years.

UCKFIELD MILL *Uckfield*
River Uck TQ 475 209 — At the lower end of the High Street.

The town of Uckfield dates back to at least 1243 and it could be presumed that a watermill was working here from that time and that as Uckfield grew in size and importance the mill was expanded to cater for the needs of the local and surrounding population. Although known as Uckfield Mill, lease agreements held in the county Record Office refer to it as Ramsleigh Mill, certainly up to 1776.

During the 18th, 19th and 20th centuries, major building additions took place here. The mill continued in operation until 1950 and, for once, it is possible to date the three buildings that make up the mill complex as each part displays a date stone. The oldest of the three buildings displays a tablet with the inscription 'CP 1792'. The initials refer to Caleb Pearce, the miller at the time, he having been the occupier of the previous mill on the site, having taken over when John Moon was made bankrupt in 1782. Pearce was still in occupation in 1824, according to an advertisement in the *Sussex Advertiser* of 25 October that year. The building erected in 1792 is built to five floors, with brick to the first floor and hanging slate for the remainder. The waterwheel was enclosed on the north side of the mill but this was subsequently replaced by an iron breastshot wheel. 18ft in diameter by 4ft 6in wide. This drove mainly iron machinery and a wooden upright shaft and, originally, 5-pairs of stones — through in its latter working days only 2-pairs were used. The most extraordinary feature of this mill was an undershot waterwheel placed in the tail water of the main waterwheel. This was meant to drive the main machinery by a belt, but was not a success and was soon abandoned.

The next building work was done towards the end of the 19th century, according to the stone tablet inscrption 'EK 1894', which refers to Edwin Kenward (who took over the family business in 1874). This was a large purpose-built five-floor building that housed a 23hp Simon Roller 2-sack mill plant powered by a Howe 24in 'Little Giant' turbine which, with a fall of 11ft, developed 25hp. The old breastshot waterwheel was retained and could be coupled to the turbine shaft when extra power was required. Through the life of this mill the power source changed to a gas engine (housed in a brick-built building at the back) and ultimately electricity. Because of the flooding that occurred here on a yearly basis, the mill was built on brick piles which raised it 4ft above ground level.

Following the erection of this building, the complex was renamed the 'Uckfield Roller Flour Mills' and this legend was emblazoned on the front wall of the mill. The last brick-built addition was erected between the two extant buildings and replaced a small and mainly wooden three-floor building. The new mill displayed a date stone with the inscription 'EW & Son 1922', and refers to Ebenezer Warburton, who had taken over the mill from the executors of Edwin Kenward in 1907. It would appear that this building was used primarily for storage and to house various cleaning and dressing machines. At this time Warburton also had control of the nearby Hempstead Mill and Buxted Mill. The 1940s saw the decline in demand for wholemeal flour in favour of white bread and the mill became wholly concerned with producing ground oats for the chicken fattening industry in the Heathfield area, with the oats imported from Canada and delivered direct to the mill from the neighbouring railway line. During World War II, the mill delivered imported white flour to the bakers in the district, with the flour being stored in a row of half-built shops in Uckfield High Street. After the war, the waterwheel along with the turbine continued to be used for oat crushing, although the electric generators were used when the river level dropped to an unworkable height.

Over the years, Uckfield Mill was conveniently placed for the conveyance of corn and flour, standing as it does near the former Ouse Navigation at Shortbridge and to Uckfield railway station. The mill closed in 1950 and the buildings were taken over by a removal company but, in 1987, the mill buildings were sympathetically renovated and converted into offices with the outward appearances retained. This Grade II listed building lies upstream of the old A22 road bridge, with the miller's cottage set into the adjacent sandstone cliff face. The River Uck, channelled above the mill, now thunders ineffectively through the site.

ISFIELD MILL *Isfield*
River Uck TQ 448 182 — North of the village near Isfield Place.

This is a mill that has been extended over the years but is now in a poor condition, though there is enough machinery inside to indicate that this was once a large commercial concern. The mill in its latter working days produced just animal feed, using electricity, and also provided storage but, by 1995, it had finally stopped working.

This does not appear to be an ancient mill site, but it was certainly in existence by 1783, according to Yeakell and Gardner's map. The central part of the present building is original and the later corrugated extension on its northern side provided the initial storage before new buildings were constructed at the back of the mill. The mill also had its own bread oven, but this building was later enlarged and used for storage. The first documented reference appears in 1803, when Edward Heaver, the miller, could supply eight sacks of flour daily, according to the Defence Schedules. The mill remained within the same family until 1874, when the following notice appeared in the *Sussex Advertiser* of 22 September that year:

'Isfield Mill. Messrs Blake & Verrall having succeeded to the business hitherto conducted by Mr Benjamin Heaver, at the above mill, beg to announce that they will continue the same from the 29th September when they will be happy to receive the patronage of all who may be disposed to favour them with their orders.'

Initially, Benjamin Heaver's son was reported to be taking over the running of the mill, but he became the miller at Upton's Mill at Framfield instead. The proposed intentions of Messrs Blake and Verrall to run the mill did not last for, in 1878, Edward Heaver had taken over the mill, according to *Kelly's* directory of that year. William Medhurst took over in 1882, with his son continuing until the turn of the century, after which William Hemsley continued for a few years. Hemsley was also the proprietor of the grist side of the business at Barcombe Old Mill. The rather grandly named 'Isfield Milling & Baking Co' purchased the mill in 1905, with Edward Sinden, a brewer by trade, becoming the proprietor. The new company installed a double horizontal 'British Empire' turbine, manufactured by Joseph J. Armfield & Co, while at the same time the mill was enlarged by an extension, which was used for storage.

The mill was later sold, in July 1912 and again in 1915, with William Hemsley back in possession. The family remained here, with Frank Hemsley relinquishing the mill in 1934. By 1938, Dickson & Church were operating here, running this mill in conjunction with Brambletye Mill at Forest Row. They fitted a new replacement turbine in 1946 and the mill became known for its 'Sussex Ground Oats' and balanced pig and poultry meal.

The inside of the mill is empty apart from some obsolete and disused machinery, but there is an abundance of support timbers on the ground floor, which is not surprising as it contained 7-pairs of stones, three of which were worked in line by a layshaft. This system, virtually intact, with its control panel, is a superb example of its type and — together with the turbine — could probably work again. Where the turbine drive enters the external wall of the original mill, the old discarded pit wheel can be seen, a relic from the days when the mill was powered by a large breastshot waterwheel. On the top floor is to be found a complete sack hoist system working on the slack belt principle, while on the floor below is a rather elaborate grain cleaner. Also, a rather nicely preserved 'miller's convenience' is to be found on the down side of the old wheelpit!

The mill has changed ownership recently and work to convert it into a house has already started. The sympathetic conversion of this mill ensures its continued existence for, without restoration, the mill would have degenerated and probably fallen into complete disrepair in a short time, and would probably have been demolished. The turbine and its associated gearing are to remain *in situ*, but the layshaft system is to be removed, hopefully to a mill museum.

The mill was powered by a leat from the River Uck, just upstream from its confluence with the River Ouse, and there is still a fair supply of water passing through. In close proximity to this mill were two other watermills, Isfield Old Mill and Isfield Paper Mill, the latter of which used the then navigable River Ouse for the transfer of materials to Lewes. When the railway to Isfield was opened in October 1858, any thoughts of using the Navigation were shelved.

Isfield Mill is an interesting and imposing building of flour floors of red brickwork, under a tiled roof. A large three-storey lucomb dominates the front of the mill and its external fabric is showing signs of age, but cracks in the brickwork are of no real concern as the mill walls are 2ft thick.

The future of Isfield Mill is now secure and although it changed with the times over the years to stay in production, it was a contest it finally lost.

OTHER MILLS ON THE RIVER UCK

EAST HOATHLY MILL
TQ 543 187

This mill disappeared in the early years of the 19th century. According to Yeakell and Gardner's map of 1783, the mill building was set below a pond. In March 1792, the *Sussex Weekly Advertiser* reported a break-in at the mill. The site lies two miles to the northeast of East Hoathly, near to Holmes Farm.

HALLAND OLD MILL
TQ 501 160

Nothing is known about this mill, which lay to the southeast of Halland, near to the source of a small stream that rises near a plantation called 'Bog Shaw'.

LEFT: The disused Stone Mill in September 1938 (AS) and RIGHT: in 1991 converted into a house. BELOW: Huggett's Furnace Mill in July 1939, now also converted into a house. (AS)

ABOVE: The waterwheel and BELOW: wooden machinery at High
Hurstwood Mill in April 1939. (both AS)

LEFT: High Hurstwood Mill in 1991. RIGHT: The unusual tile hung Buxted Mill in 1991. BELOW: The remains of the waterwheel and pentrough at Buxted Mill in 1991.

ABOVE: George Parris (on left) the miller at BELOW: Tickerage Mill,
still in work in 1896. (BT)

LEFT: The small and rather insignificant Pounsley Mill in June 1939.
(AS) RIGHT: Upton's Mill and waterwheel in June 1939, (AS) and
BELOW: An early view in the 1890s.

ABOVE: The Armfield turbine gate controls at Isfield Mill in 1991.
LEFT: The attractive front entrance to Hempstead Mill and RIGHT:
Isfield Mill at work in March 1939.

112

ABOVE: Uckfield Mill in 1910 showing three different building styles,
(BH) and BELOW: converted into offices and photographed in 1991.

113

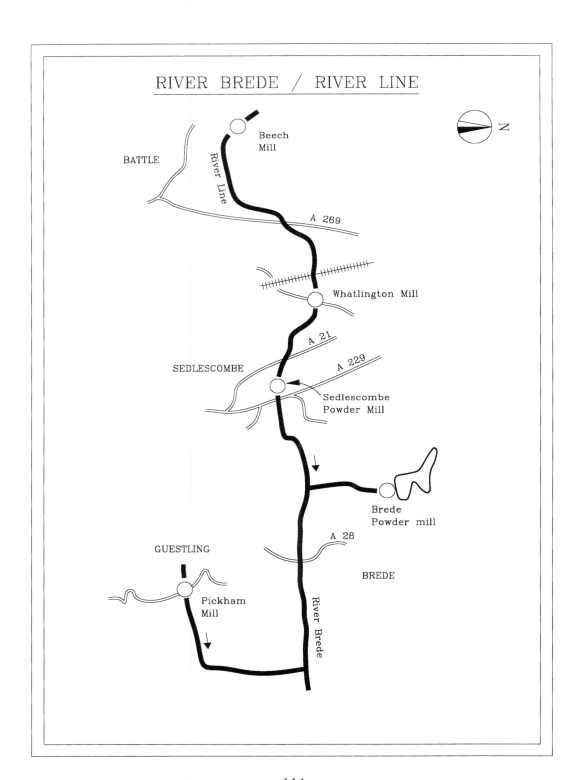

RIVER BREDE / RIVER LINE

RIVER BREDE/RIVER LINE

BEECH MILL *Battle*
Tributary to River Line TQ 727 167 — At the end of Wadhurst Lane one mile west of Battle.

This site was used as a furnace for the iron industry within an area predominantly known for its gunpowder mills. The site lies northwest of the Battle to Netherfield road, between Great Beech (a house dating back to 1600) and Beech Farm.

It appears that a furnace was working here in 1574 and probably continued into the latter years of the 18th century, while later on a corn mill was erected on the site.

John Shaw was the tenant from 1832 until 1862, but little else is known about this site apart from the fact that it was marked as 'disused' on the 1873-4 Ordnance Survey 25in map. The mill was also marked on a later map of 1928, even though the mill had been demolished before the turn of the century.

The large and attractive millpond is the only indication of the site of a long forgotten watermill.

WHATLINGTON MILL *Whatlington*
River Line TQ 761 184 — Next to Mill Lane.

The watermill at Whatlington no longer exists but, by all accounts, it was a fairly large mill that was using auxiliary power assistance in the latter years of the 19th century.

It is not known whether this was an ancient mill site, but even a small village would have supported a mill over the centuries.

Nevertheless, the first recorded documented reference appeared in 1775, in a sale advertisement that appeared in the *Sussex Weekly Advertiser* in December of that year. James Ades was the occupier of the mill in 1805, for in that year he insured the mill house and utensils for a total of £550. The fire insurance policy also makes reference to this 'corn windmill house' at Sedlescombe, together with the utensils within the windmill there.

Ades worked the mill until his death in 1830, after which the mill was taken over by William Bates, who was followed by a succession of different millers when he left in the 1860s. By 1875 a steam engine was providing the necessary auxiliary power when the water supply was poor. A sale advertisement in the *Sussex Advertiser* in May of that year gives an insight into the composition of the mill:

'Whatlington Water and Steam Power Mills. To be sold by auction at the Royal Swan Hotel, Hastings on the 12 June 1875. The Water and Steam Mill comprises three floors, having two pairs of French and one pair of Peak stones, with all necessary machinery for driving the same by a 12 foot overshot water wheel, or a fixed steam engine: and the storage room is capable of receiving 400 quarters of corn. There is a shed from whence the flour can be loaded free from wet, and engine, coal, and implement shed. Apply Solicitors.'

After Bates left the mill it was occupied by Thomas Weston and then William Ashby, who was using it until at least 1905. According to the 1907 *Kelly's* directory, the occupier was William Jenner, who apparently had the windmills at Battle, Guestling, Baldslow and Fairlight in addition! The last reference to a mill here is found in the directory of 1922 and, although it was still standing disused in 1931, it was evidently demolished after the war. Today, the site of the mill is clearly visible, with the dried-up millpond, wheelpit and some foundations set in ornamental gardens. On the opposite side of the road from the mill is the mill house, an attractive Georgian building that has recently been restored.

SEDLESCOMBE POWDER MILL *Sedlescombe*
River Brede TQ 781 177 — By the side of the A229 to the south of Sedlescombe.

Unlike many powder mill sites, there are sufficient remains at Sedlescombe to indicate the actual working area, located to the west of the mill house.

The *Sussex Weekly Advertiser* of 3 November 1761 reports an explosion (a common hazard) — this time without loss of life. Mr Harvey is identified as the occupier. Harvey was still here in 1811 when another explosion was reported, again without loss of life. This time the fabric of the mill suffered, according to a newspaper report: 'No damage was done except to the roof of the mill, which was generally stripped off.'

The small powder mill continued well into the 19th century, with Charles Laurence the occupier in 1843, according to the Tithe Apportionment. He also controlled the extensive Battle Powder Mills at the time. The powder mill buildings are marked on the Ordnance Survey 6in map published in 1871 and, later, in 1928 (although the mills had closed down in 1874, at the same time as those at Battle).

Despite the fact that the waterways have been altered slightly since the closure of the powder mill, the route of the tail race can be clearly discerned. A brick arch over it bears the inscription: 'WGH 1806', obviously referring to a member of the Harvey family. Also to be seen is an impressive 'double' weir, two large edge runners and some brickwork footings of a building connected with the powder mill.

The powder mill was situated on the southern edge of the village of Sedlescombe — a location that must have been regarded by the local residents with understandable concern!

BREDE POWDER MILL *Brede*
Tributary to River Line TQ 800 193 — West of Powdermill Lane one and a half miles west of Brede.

There is no evidence to suggest that this is an ancient mill site, as the first references here (in 1578) relate to an iron furnace. Until as late as 1717 vast quantities of iron were being produced. The site was closed down in 1766, after which it was converted for the manufacture of gunpowder. One of the principal attractions was the use of the nearby River Brede, which by then was navigable.

The gunpowder mill was operating in 1769 under the direction of Messrs Durrant & Jeakin, and in April 1781 a description of the mill appeared in the *Sussex Weekly Advertiser*, when it was offered for sale as follows:

'To be sold by Auction on the 7th June 1781, at the George Inn, Battle. The lease of which there are 17½ years unexpired of two exceedingly good gunpowder mills, and other useful buildings used with the said mills, situate at Brede, near Battle. The rent of the mills are £20 per year. The mills are supplied by a large head or stand of water, and the gunpowder made at them is held in great esteem.'

As with all gunpowder mills, explosions were frequent, as the *Sussex Weekly Advertiser* graphically reported on 16 July 1787:

'On Wednesday last, between 10 and 11 o'clock in the forenoon, Brede Powder Mill, belonging to Messrs Brooke, Jeakens & Co, blew up, by which accident two men that were in it at the time, were most miserably burnt, one of which languished till next day and died in great agony. A powder mill at the same place blew up some years ago, when one man was blown to pieces.'

In 1808 the mills were rebuilt following another explosion, while another took place in 1817, when two employees were killed. In 1825 the gunpowder mills were advertised for sale, but they remained unsold and the site was closed down and the buildings demolished. The millpond was later drained and used as a hop garden until Hastings Corporation flooded the valley in 1929 and created a reservoir, for which use it remains today. It lies just to the north of a road that connects Sedlescombe with Goatham Green, but of the mill there is nothing to be seen.

PICKHAM MILL *Guestling*
Tributary to River Brede TQ 863 151 — One mile southwest of Icklesham.

This is the most easterly of the watermill sites in East Sussex and is situated some four miles northeast of Hastings. The site is well-hidden, situated in a small valley and approached by a narrow and winding country lane. A close inspection of the site reveals the unmistakable position of the pond embankment where the wheelpit formerly stood.

The 1873 Ordnance Survey 25in map shows a large millpond here, with the mill marked as 'Corn'. A drawing of the last mill, by Charles Graves in 1865, shows it to be of ancient construction, timber framed with a thatched roof and a clasp arm overshot waterwheel. This is certainly a very ancient site, as there are references to a watermill here before the Norman Conquest, and since then a succession of mills have stood here. In 1803 the Defence Schedules referred to both a wind and watermill working in conjunction under the control of William Choak, but there are few other references to the site and it was not marked on later Ordnance Survey maps.

Pickham Mill has faded into obscurity and the former mill house was converted into two farm cottages in 1966 when the Ashburnham family sold the site, but since then it has been converted back into one dwelling. The dried-up millpond acts as a mute reminder of the extensive use of this peaceful site over the centuries.

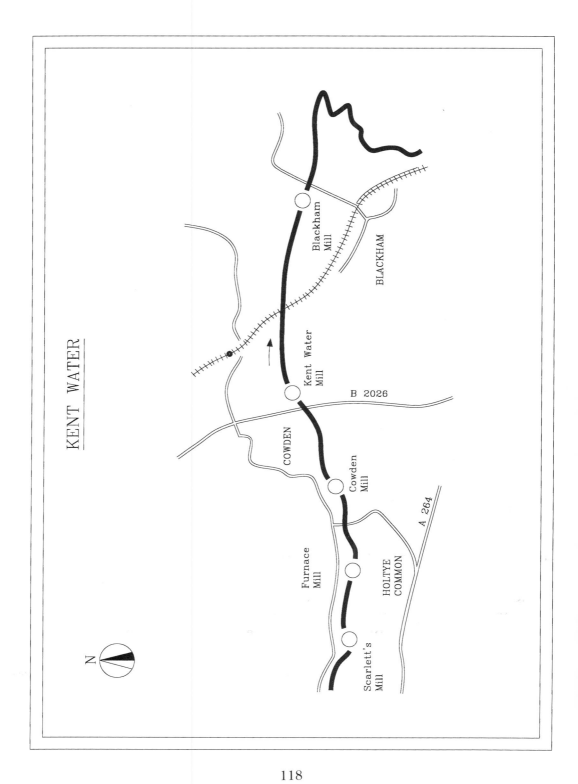

KENT WATER

N

Scarlett's
Mill

Furnace
Mill

HOLTYE
COMMON

A 264

Cowden
Mill

COWDEN

B 2026

Kent Water
Mill

Blackham
Mill

BLACKHAM

KENT WATER

SCARLETT'S MILL *Cowden*
Kent Water TQ 443 400 — South of unclassified road two miles west of Cowden.

This site was (like its near neighbour Furnace Mill) shared with Kent, with half of the waterwheel in each county. There was an iron furnace here in the middle of the 16th century, while later, in 1664, guns and shot were being produced. In an excavation by the Department of the Environment the remains of a gun casting pit was discovered at the foot of the pond embankment. It appears that the iron furnace was still in existence in 1703, for it was reported that a great storm had caused considerable damage to the buildings here. This obviously signalled the end of the iron industry for, in 1707, the site had been converted to corn milling, and it continued as such.

The corn mill continued in operation until at least 1905, when Henry Chadwell was the occupier, according to *Kelly's Directory* published that year. No doubt the mill was used for other related services, such as chaff cutting, for some years after but no commercial flour milling was carried out. Another great storm, reported in the *Sussex Advertiser* of 15 June 1889, caused problems: 'the water rose so rapidly that it swept right through the mill, the damage done being considerable.'

By 1939 Straker reported that the mill was disused, that the iron waterwheel had lost most of its buckets and that the building was being used for storage. By 1951 all the machinery was removed. The final irony for this mill occurred in September 1958, when another great storm 'dislodged' the mill, necessitating its removal soon after on safety grounds.

The only evidence found today is the millpond, which is still cared for by the owner of nearby 'Scarlett's', a grand and impressive ironmaster's house dating from 1571. Silting was such a problem here that the millpond was only returned to its former glory after the removal of 35,000 tons of silt in 1976.

The wheelpit still remains, along with the cast iron feeder pipe. From a site measurement, the waterwheel was approximately 14ft in diameter. Scarlett's Mill was a small three-storey mill built of stone and weatherboarding, with an entrance directly onto the stone floor of the mill from a track on the pond embankment, through which no doubt storm water discharged, leading to its destruction.

FURNACE MILL *Holtye*
Kent Water TQ 455 399 — Beside Furnace Pond half a mile northeast of Holtye.

The large millpond here advertises the fact that this site was previously used for the iron industry. Records indicate that there was a furnace here in 1574, under the control of Michael Weston. A 1748 map shows a furnace at the northern end, with a boring house at the southern end.

Following the demise of the iron industry, the extant mill was erected in about 1786, and there would have been few problems with water supply from the 30-acre pond although, conversely, flooding must have been a danger here at times.

This is a large buiding, containing living accommodation and comprising three storeys of brick and timber under a tiled roof. The mill is set in the pond embankment, with a loading door from the road to the top floor of the mill. It is an attractive and typically characteristic building that, despite its conversion to a house in 1931, could be nothing other than a watermill. The mill lies on the county boundary, with the mill in Kent and the former waterwheel in Sussex!

The mill is devoid of machinery, and even the tail race from the former overshot waterwheel has been incorporated into the landscaped garden. There appears to have been a succession of millers here throughout the 19th century, with Thomas Martin the last occupier, in 1895. The mill was recorded as in operation until the beginning of World War I, but thereafter it ceased work altogether.

COWDEN MILL *Cowden*
Kent Water TQ 466 402 — At the end of a private access in Cowden.

The former mill has been converted into a private dwelling and there are traces of the brick arched wheelpit wall evident, indicating an enclosed waterwheel. Prior to the contruction of the corn mill, an iron furnace was established here until it was abandoned in 1664.

There are few references to the mill, but one of the earliest was when the lease was advertised in the *Sussex Weekly Advertiser* of August 1773. Between 1828 and 1841, William Coomber was here, while the Tithe Apportionment refers to James Holland as the occupier. Charles Holmdean appears to have been the last miller before 1876 when, according to the Poor Rate, it ceased operation.

KENT WATER MILL *Cowden*
Kent Water TQ 475 405 — East side of the Hartfield Road half a mile east of Cowden.

By all accounts this was a picturesque watermill, with a profusion of white weatherboarding. A previous mill was mentioned in the will of William Turner in 1512, and later in 1772, when Richard Turner held it.

During the 18th and 19th centuries there was a succession of millers here, with William Newton the most interesting. He was described as a miller, shopkeeper and shoemaker. The last miller was David Honour, who worked this mill in conjunction with Edenbridge Mill until its closure in 1934.

The mill was of typical regional construction, being built of brick and weatherboarding under a tile roof with a projecting lucomb. The external iron overshot waterwheel, 10ft by 10ft, drove iron machinery and 2-pairs of stones.

According to Straker, writing in the *Sussex County Magazine* in August 1939, the mill had gone — apparently destroyed by fire. Odd pieces of brickwork, together with the pond embankment, indicate the position of the mill, while the Kent Water now meanders through the site.

BLACKHAM MILL *Blackham*

Kent Water TQ 501 404 — On the west side of a minor road south of Hobbs Hill Farm.

Blackham Mill was just one of five watermills on Kent Water between Holtye and Ashurst and must have suffered at times from competition. Why there were so many watermills in this rural area is mystifying. It is assumed that Royal Tunbridge Wells provided the source of demand for flour from these mills, as there were only two others in Sussex — Groombridge and Benhall — that were nearer.

It is doubtful that this was an ancient mill site as Blackham was never a village as such, but more a rural community. The Tithe Apportionment of 1843 records George Chapman as the miller but by 1851 Thomas Richardson had taken over (in the event, only for a few years). From 1858 to 1903 the mill was under the control of the Harding family, after which George Bean took over until 1918. It would appear the mill was being slowly run down, although Thomas Caffyn continued to use it until 1930, after which it quickly became disused. Straker records in 1939 that: 'A few years ago the little Blackham Mill was standing in a ruinous condition; it has recently been pulled down.'

So ended Blackham Mill, and little is to be seen now apart from the remains of the pond embankment which, according to the 1873 Ordnance Survey 25in map, was quite small. The mill had a wooden breastshot waterwheel and predominantly wooden machinery. It was, by all accounts, a delightfully attractive 16th-century building.

OTHER MILLS ON KENT WATER

BLACKHAM EAST MILL
TQ 513 400

This mill is marked on Yeakell and Gardner's map and is also shown on Greenwood's map of 1823. It was situated on Kent Water close to its confluence with the River Medway.

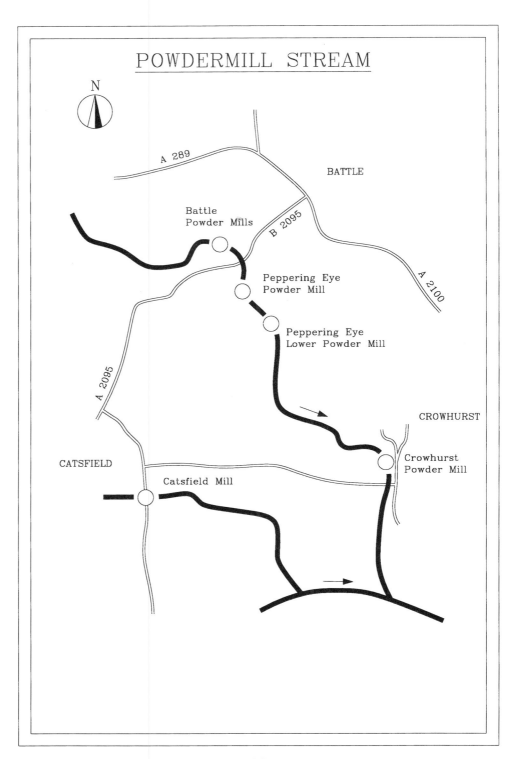

POWDERMILL STREAM

N

A 289

BATTLE

Battle
Powder Mills

B 2095

Peppering Eye
Powder Mill

A 2100

Peppering Eye
Lower Powder Mill

A 2095

CROWHURST

Catsfield Mill

Crowhurst
Powder Mill

CATSFIELD

POWDERMILL STREAM

BATTLE POWDER MILLS *Battle*
Powdermill Stream TQ 742 146 — Just north of Powdermill Lane one mile south of Battle.

In the grounds of Powdermill House are the remains of one of the largest gunpowder mills in the country, which flourished here from 1676 until 1874.

The mill site still exudes power, as there is a considerable fall of water from the existing pond and the general air of a prolific and famous industry that must have dominated the locality. It was during the middle of the 18th century that the reputation of the mills was at its highest. This mill, along with others in Sussex, was renowned for the quality of its gunpowder. A special dispensation was made in the 1772 Explosives Act to allow the continued use of pestle mills at Battle, which were generally prohibited elsewhere, and Daniel Defoe mentioned that it made the 'finest gunpowder in Europe'. The Duke of Wellington visited the mills when he was stationed with his troops at Hastings in 1806. Previous to gunpowder manufacture, the site was used for producing iron as, in 1652, there was a furnace here.

Eventually steam power was applied and a Boulton and Watt beam engine was installed when problems were experienced with the water supply.

The site was also known as 'House Mill' to differentiate it from 'Farthing Mill' (about half a mile upstream), which appeared to work more often in conjunction with the larger gunpowder mill.

There are many references to both mills during the 18th and 19th centuries but the predominant characteristic was the recording of various explosions here, sometimes with loss of life. As an example, the *Sussex Weekly Advertiser* of 30 April 1798 recorded the following:

'On Wednesday last, about twelve o'clock at noon, one of the Battle Powder mills belonging to Mr Harvey, and a drying house and store room nearly adjoining, were blown up with two tremendous explosions and totally destroyed.'

Greenwood shows two mills either side of the road but contemporary records would appear to confirm that both Battle Mill and Peppering Eye Mill were under separate ownership when William Harvey was declared bankrupt in 1817 — but not so in the middle of the 19th century, when Charles Laurence was the occupier.

The powder mills closed down in 1874 when the Duke of Cleveland, the owner of the Battle Abbey estate, refused to renew the lease because of the constant danger of explosions. Following a period of inactivity at this site, Powdermill House became a stylish residence and, in more recent years, a hotel of some elegance. In the garden, by the swimming pool, stands the base of what was once a 30ft high chimney, which formed part of the drying house, but apart from this little else remains. It is now hard to imagine the smoke and fumes that would have been emitted from this site in what is now a tranquil and peaceful setting in a deep wooded valley.

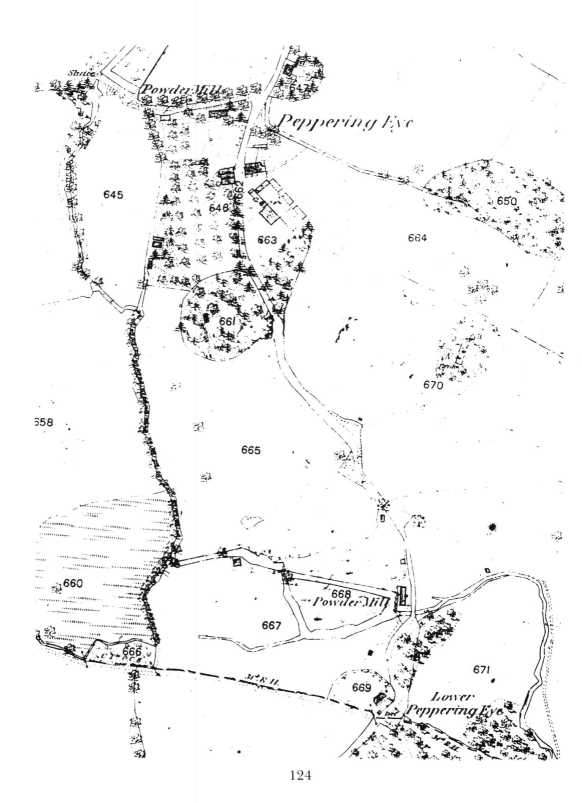

Stuica

Powder Mill

Peppering Eye

645

646

662

650

663

664

661

670

658

665

660

668 *Powder Mill*

667

666

671

669

Lower Peppering Eye

124

PEPPERING EYE POWDER MILL *Catsfield*

Powdermill Stream TQ 744 140 — Northwest of Peppering Eye Farm, one mile east of Catsfield.

This mill was an early possession of nearby Battle Abbey. In November 1676 four parcels of land (known as 'Pepperingeye') were let to John Hammond of Battle for the erection of a powder mill.

Although this site is more commonly known for gunpowder, there was a corn mill here previously (there is no evidence that they both worked in conjunction).

Although once a separate concern, by 1817 the five gunpowder sites were amalgamated under the direction of Mr Gill, but shortly after Mr Laurence took control. In 1874 all gunpowder production ceased at Peppering Eye as at all the other nearby sites. Previously to that, as at all gunpowder mills, explosions were a common occurrence — as evidenced by a report in the *Sussex Weekly Advertiser* of September 1823:

'About 6 o'clock on last Monday morning, the sifting of graining house of the powder mill at Pepper Eye, near Battle, belonging to Mr Laurence, was blown up with a frightful explosion and two men unhappily killed. The bodies of the unfortunate deceased were found at a considerable distance from the site of the demolished building, which contained about 3cwt of gunpowder. The explosion was heard at Hastings but we believe no one can tell by which accident it was occasioned.'

The site at Peppering Eye can still be traced, as the dried-up millpond and brick-built weir are evident, while a pair of edge runners have been laid out in the back garden of Peppering Eye Farm. When a large corning house was built here it was fitted with modern plant and was worked by steam power (this building still stands, now without purpose).

The site can be found west of a track that leaves the B2095 almost directly opposite the access to Battle Powder Mills, but it is difficult to visualise how different this rural and peaceful corner of Sussex was over 150 years ago.

PEPPERING EYE LOWER POWDER MILL *Catsfield*

Powdermill Stream TQ 743 136 — South of Peppering Eye Farm, one mile east of Catsfield.

This was the smaller of the two gunpowder mills at Peppering Eye, but all traces of it have now disappeared.

The 1874 Ordnance Survey 25in map shows a small triangular-shaped millpond downstream from the larger site and designates it as a 'Powder Mill'. Powdermill Cottage overlooks the site, while the datestone '1806' is to be found on the bridge where the tail race from the millpond crossed under the unmade track.

CROWHURST POWDER MILL *Crowhurst*

Powdermill Stream TQ 759 119 — Northeast of Chapel Hill, Crowhurst.

There was a forge at Crowhust in 1574 (held by John Relfe) and later, in 1664, a furnace for the making of guns and shot — though by this time the forge had been dismantled.

At some point the site was converted for gunpowder production, and it was marked as such on the 1813 Ordnance Survey 1in map. Meanwhile, an explosion took place at this site in May 1822, according to a report in the *Sussex Weekly Advertiser*:

'Early on last Monday, the Sifting House belonging to the Powder Mill at Crowhurst, in this county, the property of Mr Laurence, blew up with an explosion that greatly alarmed the neighbourhood, by which accident one poor man, named Peacham, was unhappily killed. The deceased only being in the house at the time it blew up.'

Gunpowder production continued during the occupation of Mr Laurence, and the site is marked on the 1873 Ordnance Survey 25in map.

The mill site is difficult to find, and the only clue is the property called 'Powdermill House', which is next to a minor road that leads southwards from the village centre. The stream runs immediately below the 'Mill House' at the bottom of the garden, but there are no remains to be seen.

CATSFIELD MILL *Catsfield*
Watermill Stream — tributary to Powdermill Stream TQ 734 116 — On the east side of Watermill Lane, one and a half miles southeast of Catsfield.

As the stream has been diverted away from the former mill site, it has little association now with its past. There was an iron furnace 200 yards upstream of the site but it does not appear to have interferred with the operation of the corn mill.

A mill was granted in 1536 with a pond, sometimes a meadow, indicating that it was then not very old. Although it certainly ended its working days as a corn mill, there was a suggestion that the site was used as a fulling mill, but this supposition is incorrect.

The former mill has been demolished but it once formed part of a pleasant group of associated buildings, with the miller's cottage and the mill house close by. The mill house is of three floors, with brick and white weatherboarding and an unusual cross-ridged roof. Affixed to the front of the building are the initials 'BW', fabricated in cast iron — a reference to Benjamin Wrenn, who was the miller here in 1799 (according to a fire insurance policy issued in that year). Frederick Wrenn took over the mill from 1840 and for the rest of its working life it remained in the same family, with Charles Wrenn the last miller before its closure in 1895. The Wrenns also worked Catsfield windmill for many years until it too became an uneconomic proposition.

There are no remains of the watercourse or millpond and the wheelpit has been filled with builders' rubbish. A solitary french burr stone is the only tangible relic of the corn mill.

OTHER MILLS ON POWDERMILL STREAM

POTMAN'S MILL
TQ 725 117

Nothing remains to indicate this site, which was originally a corn mill. In 1772 and 1784 it was a fulling mill, an industry very late for Sussex. It stood near Potman's Place.

LEFT: The small and mainly wooden Scarlett's Mill. (VE) RIGHT:
Furnace Mill in 1991. BELOW: A drawing of the ancient Pickham Mill
in 1865. (LF)

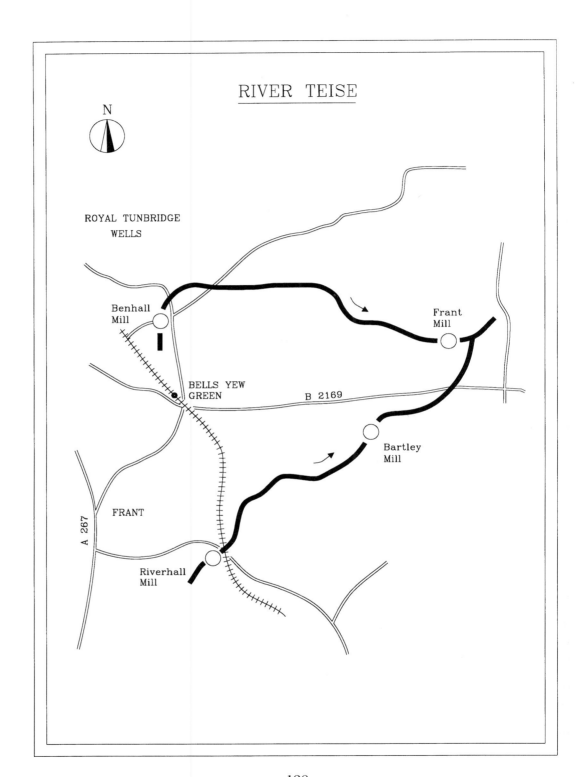

RIVER TEISE

N

ROYAL TUNBRIDGE
WELLS

Benhall
Mill

BELLS YEW
GREEN

B 2169

Frant
Mill

Bartley
Mill

FRANT

A 267

Riverhall
Mill

RIVER TEISE

BENHALL MILL *Frant*
River Teise TQ 608 376 — Next to Benhall Farm, northeast of Benhall Mill Road.

This was another watermill that was erected following the demise of the iron industry. There was a forge here in 1574, still working in 1653 although in 1667 it was 'laid aside and not used'. Benhall Mill was erected near, or possibly on, the site of the ironworks, but it is not marked on Budgeon's map of 1724.

During the compilation of the Defence Schedules in 1803, drawn up for the purpose of arriving at the estimated quantity of flour that could be expected from the local mills in time of invasion, Richard Jones, the miller, was willing to supply two sacks of 280lb of flour every 24 hours, and to supply his own wheat. His son, Stephen, carried on until at least 1845, when Christopher and Henry Smith took over and continued as a partnership until 1870, after which Henry continued alone until 1887. There are no trade directory entries for the mill after this date, indicating the cessation of commercial milling. It appears that the mill may have continued grinding animal feed for Benhall Farm for some years after.

The mill was finally demolished in the summer of 1964 after many years of lying in a ruinous state. It had three floors, two of brick and one of wood with predominantly wooden machinery, which drove 3-pairs of stones (two peak and one burr). In its latter days the top floor was replaced by a corrugated iron roof, with entry into the mill from the road onto the stone floor.

Again, as with many other sites, no trace of the mill can be found — but its position is marked by a depression at the foot of the embankment, while on the other side of the road are the dried-up remains of a millpond.

FRANT MILL *Nr Lamberhurst*
River Teise TQ 650 366 — At the end of a track north of Bayham Abbey.

This mill site is well off the beaten track, and is located within the Bayham Abbey estate. The estate church has been converted into a house and extensive landscaping has taken place, including two new lakes used for trout fishing. Just to the south flows the River Teise and, at one point, the river bed is bricklined with odd pieces of stone masonry set into the river bank. The river is very straight here, but any suggestions that this is the site of Frant Mill are pure speculation. However, the 1874 Ordnance Survey 25in map shows a small leat leaving the river before rejoining it to the east of Clay Hill Road. The map also marks a sluice gate at its confluence with the river, probably indicating the lost lost site of Frant Mill.

To the south of the Teise stand the ruins of Bayham Abbey, and a document makes reference to a watermill within the Abbey grounds. A plan extract indicates its position. This monastic watermill, destroyed during the Reformation, should not be confused with the later mill, indicated on Budgeon's map of 1724, after which there are no more references to Frant Mill.

RIVERHALL MILL *Wadhurst*
Winn Stream — tributary to River Teise TQ 667 336 — By a private road leading off the Wadhurst to Frant Road.

This was not an ancient corn mill site as, according to Straker, it held a furnace and a forge in 1574. Straker refers to the site in his book *Wealden Iron* as having 'a large oak shoot at the bottom (pond) which poured over an overshot waterwheel. The corn mill was in existence some forty or fifty years ago'.

The mill takes its name from 'Riverhall', a large house at the south end of the millpond, and it would appear that it closed down at the end of the century. This is corroborated by the fact that *Kelly's Directory* of 1898 contains the last reference to a miller at this site.

The first, and perhaps the only, mill at this site was established here in the 18th century, obviously to make use of the more than ample water supply, which was ponded here for the iron industry.

The first documented reference to Riverhall Mill appears in the Land Tax Returns for Wadhurst, which gives Edward Bolton in residence here for the years 1738-40. For most of the 19th century, the Ashby family were the occupiers of the mill, with Thomas Ashby the last recorded miller in 1899.

Little is known about the type of watermill situated here apart from Straker's comments about an 'overshot watermill'. The 1824 Ordnance Survey 25in map shows the mill at right angles to the pond embankment, but only small in size, seemingly out of proportion to the size of the millpond. The site is a mass of tangled undergrowth, but as the mill disappeared almost 100 years ago little site evidence would now remain.

Only the Mill House survives, standing by a private road that separates it from the millpond.

BARTLEY MILL *Bells Yew Green*
Winn Stream — tributary to River Teise TQ 632 357 — On the southwest side of the road just south of the B2169 to Lamberhurst.

In 1985 Bartley Mill lay empty, devoid of machinery and generally in a poor condition. The future of the mill was in doubt until it was bought by the family firm of H. S. Pledge, who had a long tradition of milling in the Ashford area of Kent. They then set about restoring the mill.

This is without doubt an old mill site, as in 1556 Thomas Baker, a miller at 'Barkeley' Mill, was fined 4s for taking excessive toll on several occasions. The name of the mill reverted to 'Bartley' soon after, according to a report in 1583.

There were ironworks in the parish from the 16th century onwards, with forges at Verridge and Brookland. These forges were located by the side of the next road west of Bartley Mill in the direction of Wadhurst. The forges, together with the mill, were in the ownership of John Barham in 1621 and remained within the family until 1723, when Lucy Barham conveyed the greater part of the property to her nephew, George Eagles. The mill was occupied by Edward Bolton in 1728 and by John Chatfield in 1750, with his son taking over in 1770. Thomas Ashby became the occupier in 1773 and remained until 1809, eventually buying the mill. Ashby sold the mill back to Bayham Abbey in 1809 when he left the mill, with John Beazley the new tenant. The next recorded occupier of the mill was Jasper Powell, who was working here in 1842. Apart from being a miller, he was a farmer and corn and potato dealer and, according to *Kelly's* trade directory, he remained until at least 1855. The mill then passed back into the tenancy of the Ashby family, with George and then William in occupation until at least 1874. William Arnold became the miller here in 1878, after which he went into partnership with his son Walter. During their occupation of the mill, a dreadful accident happened, according to a report in the *Sussex Advertiser* of 8 July 1889, when John Payne, who was working at the mill, was found dead amongst the machinery he was repairing. Ballard & Son took over in 1905, with Thomas Boorman the last recorded miller here in 1909.

Bartley Mill continued to grind corn until just before World War I, after which the buildings became engineering workshops and then reverted to farm buildings. During its latter working days a steam engine was installed owing to the drop in water level of the Winn Stream. The tall boiler chimney was demolished after the mill ceased working and the engine room became what is now the craft shop. For many years the mill lay empty and, according to an inspection in 1960, only the waterwheel remained, with the Winn Stream running through the site unchecked. The task of restoring the old mill building to full working order was considerable and not without some problems, as a millpond had to be recreated at the back of the mill. As it was proposed to open the working mill to the public, safety measures in accordance with current legislation had to be implemented. All the necessary milling machinery had to be installed, along with a electricity supply which would act as a power back-up when the water level dropped. When flour milling commenced on 4 April 1987 it represented two years of hard work, and the mill has been in full production since then using both water power and electricity as necessary.

The internally mounted overshot waterwheel, 12ft in diameter by 4ft wide, bears the inscription 'S. Medhurst, Millwright & Engineer. Lewes Sussex — 1877', while the pentrough gate was manufactured in 1887 by Weeks & Co, of Maidstone. The pentrough operated by the miller, standing at the mill spouts, used a rather unusual system of levers and chains. A large proportion of the mill is now used as a tea room and craft shop, but this is primarily a working commercial flour mill.

Externally, the yellow brickwork gives the mill a pleasant appearance, with the buildings dating back to the latter half of the 18th century. On the opposite side of the road are to be found some old farm buildings, including oast houses which, together with the mill, form a pleasant rural scheme. It is exciting to find a mill still producing flour using traditional methods and the owner, Piers Garnham, must be complimented for his tasteful renovation.

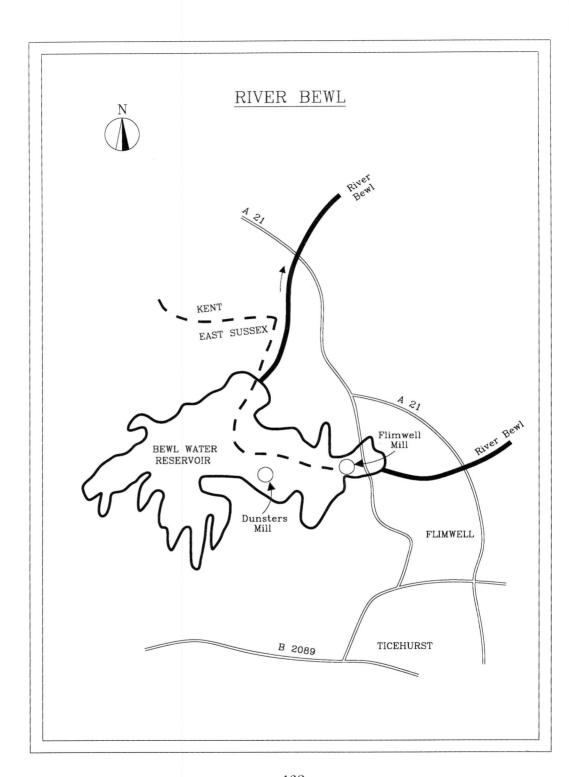

RIVER BEWL

N

River Bewl

A 21

KENT

EAST SUSSEX

BEWL WATER RESERVOIR

Flimwell Mill

A 21

River Bewl

Dunsters Mill

FLIMWELL

B 2089

TICEHURST

RIVER BEWL

DUNSTER'S MILL *Ticehurst*
River Bewl TQ 689 323 — Under Bewl Water Reservoir, northwest of Ticehurst.

Dunster's Mill was standing disused in 1940 but was still virtually complete in 1948. However, soon aferwards it was demolished, leaving only the remains of the waterwheel and some odd pieces of machinery.

When searching for the site of a mill there are usually enough remains to indicate its position, such as a wheelpit or dried-up millpond but in the case of Dunster's Mill there are certainly no visual remains, as the site lies under Bewl Water reservoir. The reservoir was constructed between 1973 and 1976 and prior to its construction the 15th-century timber-framed mill house was dismantled brick by brick and rebuilt some 1½ miles away, with the remains of the waterwheel and the layshaft also being salvaged.

There is some doubt as to the antiquity of this site, as the references to a watermill in the parish of Ticehurst in 1577, 1619 and 1796 could well refer to Witherenden Mill. On the 1813 Ordnance Survey 1in map, the mill is marked as 'Huntley's Mill' after the existing owner, while the Tithe Map of 1840 gives the correct name 'Dunster's Mill', and in the early years of the 20th century it was always known by this name. The name 'Huntley's Mill' did, though, remain in use for some years after Thomas Huntley vacated the mill in 1866. The Huntleys had owned and used Dunster's Mill for over a century, and they even constructed a windmill at Three Legged Cross as well, which was run in conjunction. The windmill was occupied for a short time during the 1850s by Charles Martin who, in about 1860, left to take over Witherenden watermill. Thomas Huntley then took over the running of the windmill and once again the two mills were back again under the control of the Huntley family.

The last, or perhaps the only, mill to occupy this site was of typical construction with one brick and two white wooden floors. It had a half-hipped tiled roof and only two floors, with an external wooden overshot waterwheel approximately 12ft in diameter, with iron sockets and buckets. The internal machinery was rather unusual, as 2-pairs of peak stones were overdriven, while 2-pairs of burr stones were counter driven. Also, the pit wheel had an extra cog row, with one shaft driving the sack hoist and another for a kibbler and crusher.

In 1872 William Orpin, who had taken over Dunster's Mill by then, installed an 8hp steam engine and boiler house but shortly after the mill was put up for sale, according to an advertisement in the *Sussex Advertiser* of 28 June 1876:

'To be sold by auction at the Auction Mart, London, on July 13, 1876. An old established Freehold and Copyhold estate known as Huntley's Mill and lands situated in the parishes of Ticehurst and Goudhurst, including the excellent Water and Steam power mills, with an 8hp engine and boiler house attached, substantially constructed about 4 years ago, having three floors, two pairs of French stones, two pairs of peak stones, flour machine, smut machine and bolter, with all the necessary machinery for driving the same by a 14ft overshot waterwheel.'

It would appear that the mill was not sold, for on 7 December 1880 the mill was again advertised for sale. The mill was taken by Henry Wickham and later by his son Harold, who remained until 1938 according to the *Kelly's Directory* published that year. Wickham was also the owner of the nearby Witherenden Mill from 1887 until 1927, and obviously prospered accordingly.

A photograph of the mill taken in 1910 shows the mill and boiler house together with a tall chimney, which no longer existed in a similar photograph taken in May 1940, two years after the mill ceased to work.

There are rather vague references to another small mill erected nearby, downsteam of the present site, but nothing definite appears to be known about this and, like Dunster's Mill, this lies hidden under Bewl Water.

FLIMWELL MILL *Flimwell*
River Bewl TQ 710 320 — Site under Bewl Water Reservoir.

Any search for the location of Flimwell Mill will end in disappointment, as the site lies submerged below Bewl Water Reservoir. It is thought that the mill was sited just into Kent, but this cannot now be verified.

Nothing is known about the mill apart from the fact that it worked in conjunction with Dunster's Mill, once situated nearby and fated to suffer a similar end.

LEFT: The partly dismantled Benhall Mill in April 1938. (FG) RIGHT:
Dunster's Mill in 1910 with its prominent boiler chimney.

ABOVE: Bartley Mill and pond in 1895 (PG) and BELOW: the mill at
work in 1991.

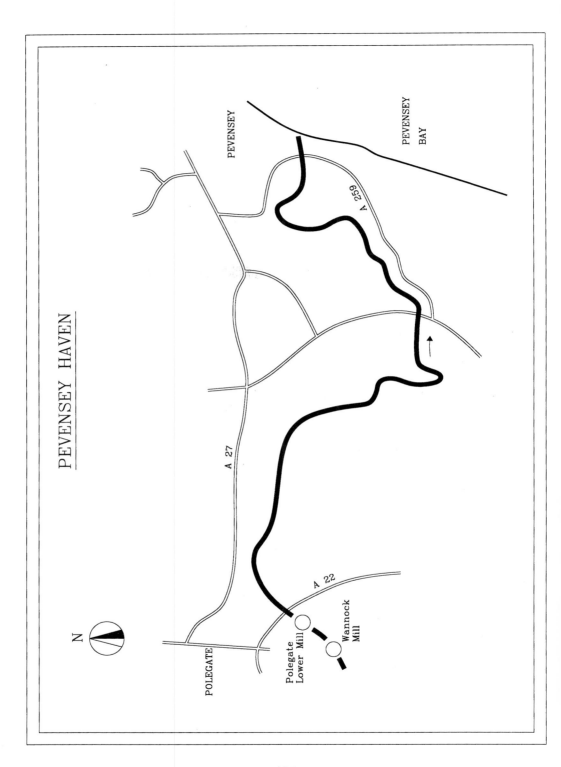

PEVENSEY HAVEN

N

POLEGATE

Polegate
Lower Mill

Wannock
Mill

A 22

A 27

PEVENSEY

A 259

PEVENSEY
BAY

PEVENSEY HAVEN

WANNOCK MILL *Wannock*
Tributary to Penvensey Haven TQ 575 035 — Next to Mill Lane, Wannock.

Wannock Mill no longer exists, having suffered a similar fate to the nearby Polegate Lower Mill, with which it worked in conjunction for many years. To illustrate the close connection between the two mills, the *Sussex Advertiser* of May 1879 refers to the sale of both watermills together with Wannock Farm, purchased by George Thomas, the sitting tenant.

The 1937 Ordnance Survey 25in map shows Wannock Mill as part of a large group of buildings that included the 'Old Mill Gardens', 'Wannock Gardens', and Wannock Farm, with a number of large greenhouses also scattered about. This is in complete contrast to the Lower Mill, which was situated on its own in open fields with only a Hospital for Infectious Diseases as company.

This is reputed to be an ancient mill site but, curiously, references only first appear in the 19th century when James Seymour came to this area from Pounsley (in about 1800) and later purchased Wannock Mill (in 1840). Seymour had built Polegate Windmill in 1817 and followed this in 1833 with the building of the Lower Mill, thus securing a complete monopoly of the flour trade in this area. George Thomas had taken over the tenancy of the mills by 1866, purchasing them in 1879. From then on, with later assistance from his sons, both mills continued working together until the Lower Mill was sold to Ephraim Ovenden in 1918. The demise of both watermills coincided in the 1890s when the Eastbourne Waterworks Company commenced pumping activities in the area. Although both watermills had millponds, the reduction in the flow of water did not help the situation. In 1920 it was reported that although the mill lay idle it was still in working condition, and also that the 'Old Mill Gardens' were open to the public.

The black tarred three-storey wooden mill was finally demolished just after World War II. It had a waterwheel similar to that at Polegate Lower Mill, but this one was 10ft in diameter by 4ft 3in wide on a square axle shaft and powered only 2-pairs of counter-geared millstones. Of special interest was the carved oak figure that once adorned the outside wall of the mill. This figure of a woman was 3ft high and painted black and white. The left hand held in front of the body a shallow curved measure and held aloft in the right hand was a substantial strike, similar in form to a rolling pin, which was used for levelling the corn in the measure. The figure was sold prior to the demolition of the mill and its present whereabouts are unknown. Beside the figure an inscription read:

'This carved oak figure is believed to be 300 years old. It represented the miller's wife of olden times with her strike and measure, which she used when poor people could not afford to pay for their gleanings to be ground. She took one gallon from every bushel of corn in payment for grinding the rest.'

The old mill house survives and reputedly dates from 1546, but a modern housing estate has been built over the site of the mill and its millpond.

POLEGATE LOWER MILL *Polegate*
Tributary to Pevensey Haven TQ 580 042 — At the end of the mill race.

There is no trace of the Lower Mill at Polegate, as a modern housing development has all but obliterated the site. For once, the date of the construction of a mill is definitely known, as it was erected by Joseph Seymour in 1933, this being substantiated by a tablet that was affixed to the mill with the inscription 'J.S. 1833'. Seymour had moved to the to the area from Pounsley and had previously built Polegate Windmill in 1817, only 300 yards away from the watermill.

Joseph Seymour used both the wind and his two watermills until about 1857, having purchased Wannock Mill in 1840, thereby having a virtual monopoly of flour milling in the area. George Thomas married one of Seymour's four daughters and continued as the miller until he purchased the freehold of both watermills and Wannock Farm following the death of James Seymour in 1879. Earlier, it was reported that, in 1870, George Thomas was in partnership here with Matthias Mockett, the latter being an interesting character who at one time ran Polegate Windmill, Wannock Watermill and the Red Lion at Willingdon! Nevertheless, later trade directories give George Thomas as the sole occupier (and owner) until October 1918, when Ephraim Ovenden took over Lower Mill together with the windmill.

Mr Ovenden came from a well-known Sussex milling family and had previously worked at the Cross in Hand and Dicker New windmills before he came to Polegate, where he worked both the windmill and the Lower Mill, although in its latter working days the watermill suffered from a lack of water. Ephraim Ovenden died in Janaury 1958, in his 87th year, and was still working until a fortnight before his death. His grand-daughter can recall him saying, when he was 85, that he must be getting old as he could no longer carry a 2½cwt bag of flour on his back! His son Albert took over the running of the mill until his retirement in 1964. Polegate windmill ceased working by wind power during the last war but continued using electricity, while the watermill carried on using waterpower until its closure in 1964.

The mill was of average size, built of brick and flint with a half-hipped tiled roof, a characteristic of house construction in this area. The waterwheel was overshot, constructed in iron, 16ft in diameter by 6ft 3in wide and manufactured by S. Medhurst of Lewes, and drove 3-pairs of stones (two peak and one burr). It must have been in good condition when milling ceased here, for the wheel was dismantled and fitted at a watermill at Wateringbury in Kent.

The mill once stood marooned on its own in open countryside and connected to the windmill by a track, but in June 1974 extensive housing development took place and the disused mill was demolished and the millpond drained.

Finding the site of the mill today is by no means easy, as there appears to be an innumerable number of cul-de-sacs within the housing estate. The site is indicated by two peak millstones set in an embankment, and although a small section of the tail race from the wheelpit can still be seen, nothing else remains of this once important and thriving watermill.

LEFT: The once isolated Polegate Lower Mill (BT) and RIGHT:
Ephraim Ovenden, the miller, in 1951. (BT) BELOW: The Lady on the
waterwheel at Wannock Mill. (BT)

139

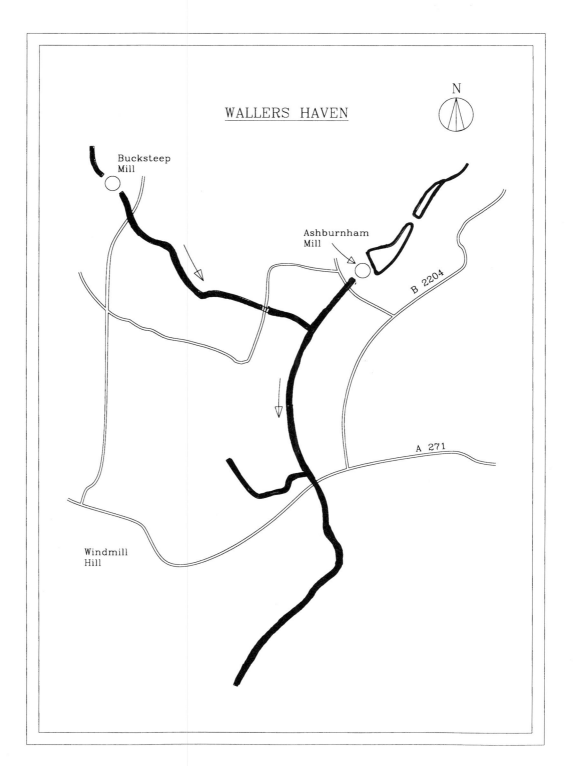

WALLERS HAVEN

N

Bucksteep
Mill

Ashburnham
Mill

B 2204

A 271

Windmill
Hill

WALLERS HAVEN

BUCKSTEEP MILL *Bodle Street Green*
Huggett's Stream — tributary to Wallers Haven TQ 654 155 — At the end of an unmade road half a mile north of Bodle Street Green.

Bucksteep Mill has long disappeared and, typically, little documentation exists to indicate the level of trade carried out here, although the site appears to have supported a flour mill through the centuries. The mill was located next to an unmade road that connects Pear Tree Farm with Tiles Farm, well off the beaten track, and is probably why the mill has remained unnoticed over the years.

The *London Gazette* in October 1862 records that the miller, James Golborne, was adjudged bankrupt until, according to an 1870 directory, the millers were Stephen & Amos Killick; four years later the former was the only occupier. Killick continued until at least 1890, while his wife was the occupier in 1895. Over the next 30 years there were four recorded millers, but it was inevitable that Bucksteep would end its days an estate mill, with Thomas Hoyland at Bucksteep Mill Farm. The mill continued working until 1934, P. J. Morris & Sons being the last occupiers.

The mill was disused in 1939. The 1899 Ordnance Survey 6in map shows a large mill pond, next to Huggett's Stream.

Recent excavations (1995) have exposed the ground floor wall and two discarded peak millstones, a concrete platform with bolts, suggesting an engine of some sort, and the single pipe feed to the former overshot waterwheel.

ASHBURNHAM MILL *Ninfield*
Ash Bourne — tributary to Wallers Haven TQ 685 143 — In the grounds of Ashburnham Place.

The watermill that once stood at Ashburnham Place was only recorded to on Budgeon's map of 1724 and nothing more is known about its past. It was replaced at some time by a water pumping mill, which continued working until quite recently. Its waterwheel has since been removed to the estate workshops, where it is being restored by volunteers. It is substantially constructed in cast iron, 6ft in diameter, and was mounted with four keys onto a wrought iron shaft and was most probably made at the nearby Ashburnham ironworks. It is intended to reinstate it back in the pond dam.

The 1874 Ordnance Survey 25in map shows a small unnamed building, probably the pumping mill, between the two ponds in front of the house, next to the ornate 1780 river bridge that separates the ponds.

Ashburnham Place was built in 1665 and, when Capability Brown landscaped the extensive gardens in the middle of the 18th century, the mill probably disappeared. The pumping mill is marked on the 1929 Ordnance Survey 6in map and the house is now a Christian conference centre.

NORMANS BAY TIDE MILL TQ 688 055

A tide mill is marked here on Greenwood's map of 1823-4. It may have utilised ponding arrangements on the Wallers Haven.

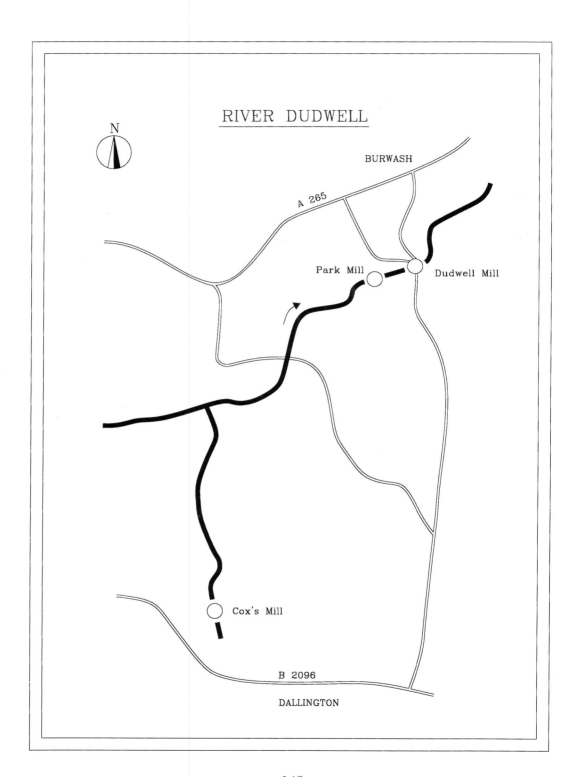

RIVER DUDWELL

N

BURWASH

A 265

Park Mill   Dudwell Mill

Cox's Mill

B 2096

DALLINGTON

RIVER DUDWELL

PARK MILL *Burwash*
River Dudwell TQ 671 236 — In the grounds of 'Bateman's' south of Burwash.

Bateman's is a large Jacobean house, built in 1634, to the south of Burwash in the valley of the River Dudwell. Rudyard Kipling became the most notable owner of the house when he purchased it in 1902, after he left India. Part of the property included Park Mill, which had ceased working by then, and it was to this mill that Kipling fitted a turbine to provide electricity to his house, until the 1920s.

Park Mill is a small three-storey brick and weatherboarded building erected here in 1795, no doubt on the site of earlier mills. The mill is worked by a small pond fed by a leat which branches off the River Dudwell half a mile upstream. The mill complex was extended in the 19th century to provide increased space for the mill and the house. This extension took place sometime between 1834 and 1861, as sale and tenancy agreements at these times refer to 2-pairs of stones and then 3-pairs of stones respectively. An inspection of the mill hursting reveals that the 2-pairs were positioned east and west, and an existing hursting was extended to carry the third stone on the south side.

Outside the mill, below the pond embankment, are the waterwheel and the turbine. The introduction of the 9ft 10in diameter waterwheel formed part of the restoration project but the turbine, installed by Kipling, was overhauled by the instructors and students of the Royal School of Military Engineering based at Gillingham. The turbine was manufactured by Gilbert Gilkes of Kendal, and is of the 'Vortex' type that produced 4hp at 280rpm. The installation of turbine and generator was carried out in 1903 by Christy Bros, who were, and still are, electrical engineers based at Chelmsford. The firm also supplied the switchboard and storage batteries, while the generator was supplied by Cromptons of Manchester. To provide lighting to his house, Kipling arranged for an electric cable to be laid underground for a distance of 250 yards, to a storage battery installation in an outbuilding. The 50 lead-acid batteries were charged in the daytime, for use at night.

The machinery inside the mill is mainly constructed in wood with the pine upright shaft and crown wheel of special interest. One pair of peak millstones is now used by the resident lady miller, who is very proud of the flour that is produced. The mill dam has a brick revetment along its downstream side, while the tail race, equal in width to the wheelpit, is bricklined for a short length below the mill.

The early history of the mill is not known, except that this may have been one of the two watermills built in Burwash between 1246 and 1248. Little else is known until 1619, when the mill is mentioned in the purchase of Park House (during which time it was known as Park House Mill).

According to *Kelly's Directory*, a succession of different owner-millers occupied the mill during the 19th century: Edward Hilder, Ephraim and Francis Russell, Samuel Barrow, William Richardson and John Skinner, who was the miller, under Richardson, until 1902. In 1968 a project to restore the mill was initiated owing to the ruinous state of the building, although most of the drive machinery was *in situ*. The roof was in a poor condition and leaking, some of the brickwork was damaged and the weatherboarding was rotten, while the stone floor had disappeared. Also, woodworm had attacked the wooden machinery and generally the site was badly overgrown and the waterways choked with weeds. The result of the restoration will be seen, and without the volunteer labour Park Mill would probably not be standing today.

The restoration of Park Mill is a splendid example of expert and volunteer labour working together to preserve a watermill that, without doubt, would have by now been added to the list of only mill sites in Sussex. The project received international recognition in 1976 when an award for 'Protecting and enhancing our Architectural Heritage' was made by the Civic Trust in association with the UK Council for European Heritage.

As 'Bateman's' is owned and managed by the National Trust, the number of visitors to Park Mill ensures that the efforts of the restoration team can ben seen and appreciated by a considerable number of people. Hopefully, some will be inspired by the unusual sight of a working flour mill.

DUDWELL MILL *Burwash*
River Dudwell TQ 677 238 — On the south side of Bateman's Lane, half a mile southeast of Burwash.

There is a vague reference to a mill here in 1347, but this cannot be substantiated to indicate that this is an ancient mill site. It was named 'Ditler's Mill' at the end of the 18th century, but it was identified under its present name on the 1813 Ordnance Survey 1in map. Dudwell Mill was one of two watermills located to the south of Burwash but, unlike its famous neighbour, Park Mill, it has disappeared without trace and been long forgotten.

The mill lay beside a leat cut from the main river, and although the mill was unexceptional in design, the method of water supply to the mill was certainly most unusual. A sluice downstream from the mill was closed, with the water overflowing backwards into the mill race, passing the wheel before rejoining the main river.

Until 1822, the mill was in the occupation of John Skinner, while two years later, John Hilder held the mill, along with Darwell Mill at Brightling and a windmill at Burwash. The 1839 Tithe Apportionment makes reference to John Honeysett here, but it is not clear when he left. Later, in May 1861, a dreadful accident took place at the mill, resulting in the death of the very popular miller, Thomas Ellis. According to a report in the *Sussex Advertiser*, Mr Ellis was crushed to death while attempting to grease machinery that was in motion. The mill was taken over by J. and H. Smith, who remained until 1887 when Richard Fuller, the tenant of the adjacent Dudwell Farm, took over the running of the mill. *Kelly's Directory* of 1903 records a George Garden Jnr as the occupier, but it is not clear whether the mill was still running. In its latter working days, the mill was mainly used for provender food, hence Fuller's interest from 1887, but no date is given for its final closure. From a contemporary photograph of the mill, it was by no means a small building. It would appear to be of three floors, weatherboarded under a half-hipped tiled roof. Its predominantly wooden construction compounded its progression to disrepair, with its demolition following in 1948.

The site is totally devoid of any remains of the mill, although the neighbouring mill house is of ancient construction, indicating its association with a previous mill here.

COX'S MILL *Dallington*
Tributary to River Dudwell TQ 652 201 — At the end of a track half a mile north of Dallington.

There is no reason to suggest that this is an old site, as the first reference to it appears on a map of 1780, when the building is shown but not named.

Little is known about the mill, which is not surprising as it is located some distance to the north of Dallington and only reached by way of an unmade track on the edge of Dallington Forest. That the mill building remains is unusual in the first instance and it is equally surprising to find it has not been converted into residential accommodation. It was apparently used as a small warehouse some years ago, with a turbine to produce electricity, but it now remains empty and devoid of machinery.

In 1812 the *Sussex Weekly Advertiser* of 31 August reported on the death of William Saunders, of Cox's Mill. Later, on 23 August 1881, the *Sussex Advertiser* included the following:

'To be let from Michaelmas next, in the parish of Dallington, Sussex. A water mill driving two pairs of stone, with about 45 acres of land and two good cottages. Rent very moderate. For particulars apply to Mr. R. Hodgson, Ashburnham, Sussex.'

William Kingsland took up this lease, moving from Chapman's Town windmill, and stayed until at least 1890, after which there are no trade directory entries indicating occupiers of this mill.

Cox's mill is a small mill, built of brick and stone with a tiled half-hipped roof, set midway down a high pond embankment. Extensive waterwheel 'score marks' are visible on the wall beside the wheelpit which, when measured, give a wheel diameter of 15ft, while inside the mill are the remains of a concrete engine bed.

With such a large available water supply and a pond embankment 30ft high, this small mill, erected at the east end of the bay, seems rather out of place here. Just downstream from the mill is Glaziers Forge Farm, which is on the site of a wealden iron furnace and forge. This site is marked as a forge on Budgeon's map of 1724, therefore indicating that it was one of the last working forges in Sussex. As Cox's Mill was not established until the end of the 19th century, it is quite probable that the millpond was actually constructed to serve as a pen pond for the two ponds that served Glaziers Forge. This is now an idyllic site and together with the attractive mill house forms a most pleasant location.

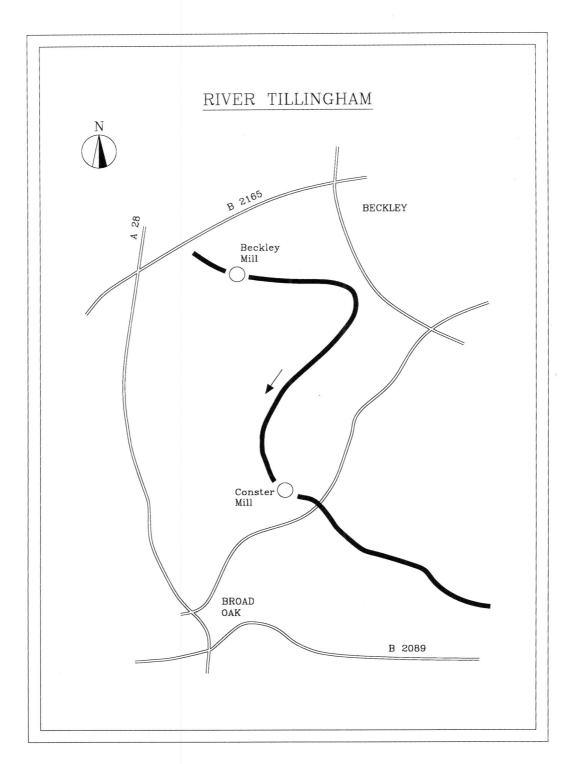

RIVER TILLINGHAM

RIVER TILLINGHAM

BECKLEY MILL *Beckley*
Tributary to River Tillingham TQ 838 228 — At the end of an unmade track leading off Watermill Lane southwest of Beckley.

This site lies at the end of an unmade road, southwest of Beckley. It is not easy to find, as all traces of the mill building have long gone and only the unmistakable pond bay gives away the position of the mill. Like many other millponds at demolished mill sites, very little water remains and most of it is now overgrown with vegetation.

It does not appear to be an ancient site and the first definite reference appears in the *Sussex Weekly Advertiser* in March 1793, when the miller, John Ashby, advertised for an assistant. A fire insurance policy dated the following year describes the mill as 'timber, plaster and thatch'. Following this very little is recorded, apart from the names of the millers, and it appears that the mill changed hands frequently in the 19th century. Thomas Body was in occupation in 1851 but after he left in 1855 Godfrey Stonham took over, continuing here to 1870. The partnership of Cooper & Bates were running the mill soon after to 1878, when the last miller, Joseph Caffyn, took control. It is not known when the mill ceased working, but the 1872 Ordnance Survey 25in map indicates the mill as 'Corn', thus signifying that by then the mill was mainly producing animal feed.

It is not known when the mill was demolished, but the miller's house remains, although this has been altered and enlarged over the years. The mill would have had an overshot waterwheel and the base of the bricklined pentrough has been cleared out by the owner. Scattered around the garden are an assortment of peak millstones.

CONSTER MILL *Beckley*
Tributary to River Tillingham TQ 836 211 — Northwest side of Furnace Lane, two miles southwest of Beckley.

This was one of the two watermills in the vicinity of Beckley and was, at times, curiously referred to as Brede watermill, presumably because of its location within that parish.

The site has a close association with the Wealden iron industry, as a forge established in 1587 was superseded by a furnace in 1653. The name 'Conster' was mentioned as early as 1599, when it was marked on Stonham's map as 'Conster Forge'.

The site lies between Conster Manor and Great Conster Farm in countryside little altered over the years. Iron production continued until at least 1744, but a report in 1787 stated that it was still standing and might work again in time of war. It is apparent that it did not work again, for in the early years of the 19th century a flour mill was erected. In 1811 it was in the occupation of Solomon Coloran, according to a sale notice that appeared in the *Sussex Weekly Advertiser* of February that year. From 1859, and probably before, Tilden Miller was the recorded tenant and he later used Brede windmill in conjunction (1887). Still retained in the same family, David and George Miller continued milling until 1911, after which trade references to the mill cease. This was due to the fire here in 1909, about which *The Miller* commented:

'A serious fire occurred last month at Brede mills, owned by Messrs D & G Miller, and situated at the Furnace, Brede. The mill was completely destroyed with its contents both of machinery and stock. The amount of the damage is roughly estimated at £1,000. The fire was first noticed shortly after 1 o'clock in the morning.'

Not all of the machinery was destroyed, for the framework of the overshot waterwheel remains near to the front door of the mill house. The wheel is 13ft 6in in diameter by 5ft 4in wide, and has a very thin iron and wood rim. The remains of the pond bay are still visible, although the river has been diverted away from the site.

ABOVE: A view of Dudwell Mill showing its unusual sluice controls with the mill building in the background. (VE) OPPOSITE ABOVE: The well known Park Mill at Bateman's in 1951, saved for the nation, (SPAB) and BELOW: not so lucky – the disused waterwheel at Dunster's Mill in May 1940. (AS)

GLOSSARY

Ark — A wooden bin for holding flour.
Axle — Shaft linking waterwheel with pit wheel.
Bedstone — The lower and fixed millstone.
Bin — Container for storing grain on the top floor of the mill.
Bolter — Used for the dressing or sifting of flour.
Breastshot Waterwheel — Wheel where the water is projected against its centre. Variations are high or low.
Bridge Tree — Beam of the hursting that supports the lower end of the stone spindle.
Buckets — Fittings around the waterwheel that hold water.
Burr Stone — Millstone quarried near Paris.
Clasp Arm — Wheel whose spokes form a square around the shaft.
Compass Arm — Wheel whose spokes radiate from the shaft.
Cogs — Removable wooden teeth of a gear wheel.
Corn — Grain or seed of any cereal crop.
Corn Laws — Regulatory statute to control the import of foreign wheat.
Crown Wheel — Cog wheel at the top of the upright shaft; drives ancillary machinery.
Dresser — Used for grading flour; wire or silk lined.
Dressing — Process for sharpening millstones when worn.
Eye — The opening in the middle of the runner stone through which grain enters.
Floats — The wooden or metal paddles on a waterwheel.
Grist — Animal feed ground at a mill.
Headrace — Section of stream above a mill, frequently referred to as a leat.
Hopper — Open topped wooden box through which grain passes to millstones below.
Hurst — Wooden framework supporting millstones and enclosing pit gearing.
Jack Ring — Mechanism for disengaging stone nut.
Leat — See Headrace.
Lucomb — A cabin projecting from the bin floor containing hoisting gear.
Mill Bill — Implement used for stone dressing, consisting of a handle and bit.
Millstones — A pair of stones made of burr, peak or composition material.
Overshot Waterwheel — Water is projected past the top of the wheel.
Peak Stone — Millstone quarried in Derbyshire.
Pentrough — Trough conveying water to the waterwheel.
Pinion — Small type of gear wheel.
Pit Wheel — The first gear wheel inside mill, affixed to axle shaft. Usually iron with wooden cogs.
Pond Bay — The dam or embankment of a millpond.
Race — Water channel above or below waterwheel.
Runner Stone — The upper millstone revolving over bedstone.
Sack Hoist — Used to raise flour or grain up and down through the mill.
Shoe — Tapering wooden trough leading from hopper to eye of millstone.
Smutter — Ancillary machine for removing diseased particles of wheat.
Spur Wheel — Affixed to upright shaft, above the wallower, engaging the stone nuts.
Stone Nut — Pinions engaging the spur wheel; keyed to pivot on which runner stone is turned.
Stone — See Millstones.
Stone Spindle — Shaft attached to runner millstone.
Thrift — Wooden handle of mill bill.
Undershot Waterwheel — Water is projected under the wheel striking the paddles.
Upright Shaft — Vertical wooden or iron shaft.
Wallower — Small toothed gearwheel affixed to upright shaft and driven by pit wheel.
Wire Machine — See Dresser.

BIBLIOGRAPHY

Bennett, R. and Elton, *History of Corn Milling* (4 vols) Simpkin Marshall 1899.
Brunskill, R. W., *The Illustrated Handbook of Vernacular Architecture* Faber & Faber 1972.
Reynolds, J., *Windmills and Watermills* Hugh Evelyn 1970.
Reid, K. C., *Watermills of the London Countryside* Charles Skilton Vol 1 — 1987, Vol 2 — 1988.
Stidder, D., *The Watermills of Surrey* Barracuda Books 1990.
Syson, L., *British Watermills* Batsford 1965.
Vince, J., *Discovering Watermills* Shire Publications 1978.
Vine, P., *Kent & East Sussex Waterways* Middleton Press 1989.
Watts, M., *Corn Milling* Shire Publications 1983.
Wenham, P., *Watermills* Robert Hale 1989.

Society for the Protection of Ancient Buildings

A hundred years ago windmills and watermills were sights so common they were hardly noticed. Today few are left, and their numbers are still diminishing. The Society for the Protection of Ancient Buildings is the only national body with a section devoted solely to the preservation of our old mills. The main responsibility of the Section is to encourage the sincere and proper repair of these mills, wherever possible to working order, so that truly authentic examples will survive for future generations to study and repair. If this book has inspired the reader in an interest in the study or appreciation of watermills in general, they may wish to join the Wind and Watermill Section of the Society for the Protection of Ancient Buildings. For further membership details contact the Section Administrator at SPAB, 37 Spital Square, London E1 6DY.

INDEX

153

154

SUBSCRIBERS

Presentation Copies

1 Society for the Protection of Ancient Buildings (Wind and Watermills Section)
2 East Sussex County Library
3 Frank Gregory

4 Derek & Moira Stidder
5 Colin & Jane Smith
6 Clive & Carolyn Birch
7 Tom Stidder
8 Barry Stidder
9 Amy Stidder
10 Stephanie Smith
11 Christianne Smith
12 D.S. Burrows, LlB, FRES
13-14 Mr Hoather
15 Peter J. Hill
16 P.S. Jarvis
17 Mrs A. Shipley
18 Jeff Sechiari
19 Alan J. Mitchell
20 John Hayes
21 Jim Woodward-Nutt
22 Douglas E. White
23 Alan Crocker
24 P.W. Wakefield
25 L.A. Barber
26 Adrian Thomson
27 Nigel Moon
28 Derek Harvey-Piper
29 D.H. Cox
30 Michael Oakley
31 W. Steer
32 K.R. Hemsley
33 E.F. Goatcher
34 A.R. Tulley
35 Simon Janes
36 Anita Hardenburgh
37 Michael John Fuller
38 Michael Yates
39 Martin Brunnarius
40 Brian J. Lee
41 R.S. Harlow
42 D.T.N. Booth
43 A. Kite
44 D.F. Filmer
45 Martin Watts
46 J. Kenneth Major
47 D.R. Bushell
48 Derek Harvey-Piper
49 Jim Woodward-Nutt
50 John Tritton Pelling
51 Josephine Duggan
52 R. Skinner
53 K.R. Hemsley

54 Jim Oliver
55 Miss D.M. Herridge
56 National Monuments Record Centre
57 Dr I.P. Crawford
58 Peter Booth
59 R. Hawksley
60 Mr & Mrs R. Proctor
61 Mrs M. Beswick
62 Martin Bodman
63 Ian M. Clark
64 John Day
65 M. Dufau
66 Mrs S.J. Grover
67 Susan Gilbert
68 L.W. Hubbard
69 Chris Clarke
70-74 S.P.A.B. Mills Section
75 G.R. Holman
76 Robert Battersea
77-78 Mrs Bertha Terry
79 John Mew
80 R.H.Thomas
81-82 Ann Turner
83 S.D. Robertson
84 M.E. Stredwick
85 K. Seabrook
86 R.G. Martin
87 E.A. Newman
88 N.D. Lewis
89 Ann M. Kitchen
90 C.G. Mackay
91 Elizabeth Blake
92 Stella Patterson
93 E.W. Henbery
94 Derek P. Grieve
95 David Tomlinson
96 Alan Stidder
97 Clara Stidder
98 Richard John Woolford
99 A.O. Brown
100 Martin Newton
101 A.A. & P.B.D. Bryan
102 Geoff & Christine Morris
103 Mrs Ann M. Vollor
104 J.M.H. Bevan
105 Simon Barrett

106 John S.F. Blackwell
107 Gary C. Bell
108 Rita J. Ensing
109 R.R. Potts
110 P.M. Pearce
111 Maev Wilkinson
112 George V. Hodges
113 James S. Tasker
114 S.W. Bartlett
115 Cecil French
116 Tim Ralph
117 Niall Roberts
118 A.F. Hill
119 Donald Burton
120 David J. Nash
121 Ton Meesters
122 Geoffrey Mead
123 Nigel J.T. Melican
124 F.W. Gregory
125 David Stuttard
126 Derrick Alan Rogers
127 Mrs Elizabeth Fairclough
128 J. Wingate, Cox's Mill
129 Barbara Bond
130 J.H.D. Smith
131 G. Cole
132 Thomas R. Dadswell
133 Michael Edwards
134 J.F.K. Lee
135 Nick Catford
136 C.W.G. Bullocke
137 N. Plastow
138 J.W. Hill
139 Paul C. Smith
140-141 A. Jarman-Price
142 Alan Stoyel
143 A.E. Bancroft
144 W.F. Strickland
145 Miss V.M. Hodsoll
146 Michelham Priory
147 Patricia F.C. Parr
148 P. Langford
149 J.G. Harman
150 David Morgan
151 R.D. Ashton
152-153 Wessel Koster
154 John Rickman
155 Mrs P. Bracher

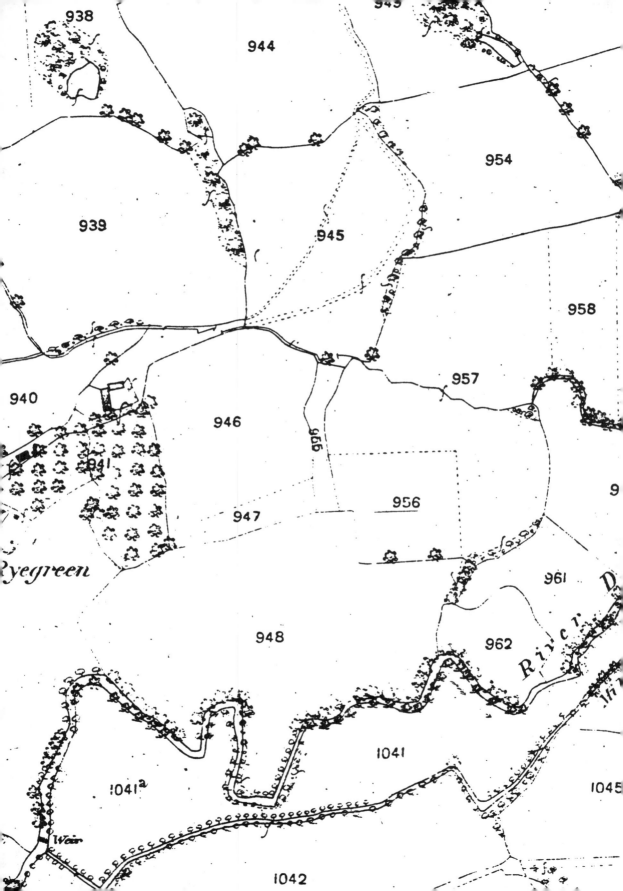